Solar Eclipses

in the Bible

Toni

 This book is a ~~token~~
small token of appreciation
for your friendship.

"Rejoice always, pray
continually, give thanks
in all circumstances;
for this is God's will
for you in Christ Jesus."
    1 Thessalonians
     5: 16-18

J Grimm

Solar Eclipses
in the Bible

By:

Jeffrey D. Grimm

Solar Eclipses in the Bible

by

Jeffrey D. Grimm

To Vonie Grimm

My wife, best friend, and companion in our walk with Jesus, who is always up for seeing new things like total solar eclipses.

PREFACE

This book began as a personal study but turned into a study for Christians seeking the truth. Two years before the total solar eclipse of 2017, I started making plans for my family to see the totality. As always, I started studying the Bible to find what, if anything, it said about eclipses. I found that the Bible contains many references to total solar eclipses. To my astonishment, several pivotal moments on the Bible timeline line up with known historical solar eclipses.

I shared my research with my friends who were taken back by the findings. Their reaction indicated that this could be a blessing to others, just as it is to my family, friends, and myself. I am moved to publish the findings out of the hope of encouraging Christians in their walk with God.

CONTENTS

Introduction

The Bible can be proven accurate by lining up biblical and astronomical events. The overlapping of astronomical and biblical events that co-occurred reveals they occurred precisely as the Bible states. This book will uncover exact biblical dates, proving that the Bible is accurate. The Bible is the primary reference for this book, and additional inputs will be taken from Bible scholars, secular historians, and scientific astronomical data. By combining all available resources, the Bible will be proven accurate.

The Sky

Thousands of years ago, natural phenomena such as solar eclipses were unexplainable. The few to witness an eclipse were left searching for supernatural answers.

Modern-day efforts attempt to prevent explainable events in nature from being ascribed to God's working of miracles. Modern-day education gives us an understanding of how nature works. However, some people believe miracles must only be explained supernaturally; otherwise, they are not miracles. Modern education raises the question: Did God do it if a miracle can be explained by science?

The New Testament answers such a question in Colossians 1:16: "For in him were all things created, in the heavens and upon the earth, things visible and things invisible, whether thrones or dominions or principalities or powers; all things have been created through him, and unto him; and he is before all things, and in him all things consist." Seeing God created everything, even natural laws, then God is the consistency behind these laws of nature making them technically miracles.

An example of this concept appears after Noah came out of the ark. God performed a miracle by placing a rainbow in the sky. Noah did not know how the rainbow had been created. He only knew it to be a sign from God. Today, science explains rainbow creation as a natural phenomenon of lightwave separation. Even though science has proven how rainbows are created, they are still miracles. God uses natural phenomena put into place at the creation of the universe to perform some miracles.

At the time of creation, God established the laws of nature. The laws of nature govern everything around us including planetary movements and natural phenomena. Job proclaimed that God created the heavens: "that maketh the Bear, Orion, and the Pleiades, and the chambers of the south; That doeth great things past finding out, Yea, and marvelous things without number" (Job 9:9-10). Seeing that God made the heavenly bodies, one would assume that He has complete control over their motion through the sky and the subsequent phenomenon resulting from that set motion. This brings the conclusion that a God who knows the future and who made all things could have built events into the creation of the world.

This book considers God as an all-knowing, omnipotent God that has the power to build miracles into creation, placed precisely in the location and time needed for the people that needed them.

Heavenly Ebenezers

A total solar eclipse can be considered both an event and an object. Eclipses are events because the viewer sees a show involving daylight turning into darkness. Equally, eclipses are objects because it is built into the permanent celestial timeline. Science can prove that eclipses occurred via astronomical calculations transforming them into objects. As a result, eclipses are both a fleeting moment and an object that will remind everyone of the event for centuries to come.

Pivotal moments in the Bible are frequently marked with objects. "Samuel took a stone, and set it between Mizpeh and Shen, and called the name of it Ebenezer, saying, Hitherto hath Jehovah helped us" (1 Samuel 7:12). This Ebenezer is a stone of remembrance. God helping Israel is an event, and the rock turned the event into an object. The Ebenezer was visible for generations to come. Joshua laid 12 stones where they crossed into the Promised Land to remind all generations of their crossing. Moses gave all 12 tribes a stone on the priest's stone plate to remind Israel of the 12 tribes. These all are fleeting moments that are marked by permanent objects.

Solar eclipses are objects recorded in the history of time as an Ebenezer symbol of God's provision. There is no way for a person to shift a solar eclipse, for it is a non-changing timeline of the stars without gaps or pauses but can be played forward or backward with the same results. The scientifically provable facts of an eclipse's location and time make them a perfect Ebenezer.

The Holy Spirit has blessed us with the knowledge of how to calculate all solar eclipse's locations and dates. We now can find locations and dates of eclipses going back to the time of Abraham. Star charts provide dates and locations of eclipses, magnitudes of the eclipses, and other valid data. Now, for the first time, one can see what our ancestors saw thousands of years ago!

August 21, 2017 AD

It is not easy to understand what one has not experienced. This is why I believe it is essential to observe an eclipse. However, if it is impossible to experience an eclipse, I offer my eclipse observations from 2017.

On August 21, 2017, my wife Vonie, my son Ben, and I went to Jackson Hole, Wyoming, to view the eclipse with my in-laws. Jackson Hole is in the middle of the Grand Teton National Park and was in the path of eclipse totality. On the morning of the total solar eclipse, the weather was in our favor. No clouds were in the sky, so I expected an unobstructed view of the eclipse. The temperature was comfortable at 70 degrees.

Below are my notes of that day:

10:16 AM: The sun was about one-third of the way up in the sky when the sun's partial eclipse started. The birds were chirping, and squirrels were playing in the trees. I did not perceive anything out of the ordinary, and I would not have known the sun was being eclipsed if I did not have my special eclipse sunglasses on.

11:09 AM: The loss of light became noticeable. I felt like someone was using a dimmer switch on the sun. I was able to see everything, but it felt like the sun was refusing to shine. I looked through my eclipse sunglasses and saw the sun was 70% covered. I took my glasses off to sneak a peek[1] at the eclipse. It looked like a thin sword of light in the sky.

11:29 AM: The temperature dropped 10 degrees, and a slight breeze started. My wife and son went to get a jacket, but I refused to leave, afraid I would miss the action. I looked through my eclipse glasses and saw the sun 90% covered. Looking around, I could sense a substantial loss of light. The sky looked like a twilight just as the sun went under the horizon, but limited light came from above instead of the horizon. The streetlight turned on as it does at sunset. A noticeable breeze pushed through the area, making me cold. I took my glasses off to sneak a peek at the eclipse. I noticed that the sun appeared to be 10/12 covered even though it was actually 11/12 covered.

11:32 AM: The magnitude of the solar eclipse was 97%. Looking through my eclipse glasses, I could only see a thin crescent of light. I took off my glasses to sneak a look at the eclipsing sun. I noticed a large black circle in front of the sun with a very bright outline like fire coming out from a black circular object. One side of the sun was visible and appeared as a crescent of fire. Looking at the ground and the house's siding,

---

[1] **Warning**: *looking at the sun without appropriate safety equipment is dangerous and can result in permanent eye damage causing loss of sight.*

5

I could see a subtle motion, the same type of motion you see when looking through a pool of water and see lines moving.

11:35 AM: The total solar eclipse came on like the flipping of a light switch. I was covered in darkness, and I found myself hollering excitedly with others that could be heard in the area. The presence of such a thunderous hollering, coupled with a fully eclipsed sun, gave the appearance of looking inside the barrel of a sounding trumpet. The sky had light, then instantaneously, no light. The breeze stopped. The temperature fell a few more degrees, leaving me shivering. I could see the light on the horizon just like the sun had gone down behind it, but it came from all around me in a 360-degree radius. It looked like a sun had set at each of the compass points. At the exact moment of darkness, I can see a short-lived flare of light explode from the side of the eclipsing sun then a flaming ring of fire that flickered.

The moon was dark; it did not give any light because it was directly in front of the sun. The sun no longer gave us light because it was hidden behind the moon. The sky was as dark as it gets on a full moon night. I was not able to see any constellations because it was too bright. I was able to see four planets: Venus, Jupiter, Mars, and Mercury. The crickets started making noises like they do every night, and crows started their evening flight home. After two minutes of darkness, another flare of light explodes from the other side of the ring of fire.

11:37 AM: After two minutes of totality, light returned to the earth just as fast as it went dark. The wind started blowing again, and the shadows bounced, making me feel like the world was moving.

13:00 AM: The eclipse was over, but the animals were all confused; the crickets were still making noises, and mice ran in the field. No wind blew.

For me, the totality of the 2017 eclipse left me speechless. The magnitude of the event was heavy. The thought of God loving us so much that He would make such an event for us to witness was overwhelming. The only thing I can compare it to is when a child sees a full bright rainbow for the first time, and their parents tell the child that God put it there to remind us that He will never destroy the world with a flood again.

1

Job's Leviathan

The book of Job is thought to be the oldest in the Bible. Within the book, Job describes the leviathan solar eclipse that occurred over Mesopotamia. This is the first mention of day turning to darkness, a reference to a solar eclipse. Job used this solar eclipse symbolically to represent the sadness of his birth. With the acknowledgment of solar eclipses and its symbolic language, the book of Job sets a precedent that is embraced throughout the Bible.

Timing

The exact years when Job lived are not known. Job is thought to have lived after the Noetic flood based on Job 22:16. About this, Ellicott's commentary states, "It is generally supposed that there is an allusion here to the history of the Flood."[2] Conversely, Job is thought to have lived before Moses based on

---

[2] Stanley Leathes, Edited by Charles John Ellicott, *An Old Testament Commentary for English Readers, vol. IV, Job* (New York: Cassell and Company, 1884), p. 41.

Job's priestly activities as the household head versus having the Levitical priest performing it (Job 1:5; 42:8). These verses are used to create a rough window of time when Job is thought to have lived.

Historians have divided into two groups over the date of Job. The early date group places the life of Job about two generations before Abraham. The late date group places the years of Job at the same time as Abraham or a few generations after.

The *Peoples Bible* notes three observations used for dating Job:

1. The long life of Job, extending to two hundred years.

2. The absence of any allusion to the Mosaic law, or the wonderful works of God towards Israel in their departure from the land of bondage, and their journey to Canaan; which are constantly referred to by the other sacred writers, as illustrating the character and government of Jehovah.

3. The absence of any reference to the destruction of Sodom and Gomorrah; which memorable event occurred in the vicinity of the country where Job resided; and which as a signal and direct judgment of the Almighty upon the wicked, would hardly have been omitted in an argument of this nature.[3]

---

[3] Joseph Parker, *The People's Bible: Discourses Upon Holy Scripture, Vol. XI, The Book of Job* (New York: Funk and Wagnalls, 1889), p. 196.

Of all the variables used to date Job, his age is debated and leveraged the most. To this, Barnes states: "The age of Job. According to this, the time when he lived, would occur somewhere between the age of Terah, the father of Abraham, and Jacob, or about 1,800 years before Christ, and about 600 years after the deluge."[4]

The majority of historians place Job's years around Abraham plus or minus a few generations. Albert Barnes wraps this up the best by saying, "Circumstances combined leave little doubt as to the time when Job lived. They concur in fixing the period as not remote from the age of Abraham."[5] This book will follow this logic and date Job between 2,000 BC and 1,800 BC.

Location

Job lived in the region that stretched from lower Canaan to Ur. The exact location where Job lived is unknown. However, it is theorized that he lived between Canaan and the Euphrates River located inside the Chaldeans' land. Job likely lived close to the city of Ur based on the Chaldeans mentioned in Job 1:17. Seeing that the Chaldeans killed his servants and stole his camels, he was more likely to be closer to the Chaldeans than the Canaanites.

Secondly, the fact that Job was acquainted with Astronomy shows he most likely lived close to Ur. In that era, astronomy knowledge came out of Ur. Those who lived in Ur would have

---

[4] Albert Barnes. *Notes: On the Book of Job, Vol. I* (New York: Leavitt, 1849), p. xvi.

[5] Ibid, p. xix.

been educated in astronomy. Job had knowledge of constellations and the story of the celestial dragon swallowing the sun. Job knew astronomy, so he most likely lived close to Ur.

Job's Knowledge

Job, like Abraham, knew about the Chaldean's teachings of astronomy. Abraham lived about the same time as Job. Abraham lived in the city of Ur of the Chaldeans before leaving with his father. Abraham was familiar with the science of astronomy. Josephus states, "Abraham communicated to them arithmetic, and delivered to them the science of astronomy; for, before Abram came into Egypt, they were unacquainted with those parts of learning; for that science came from the Chaldeans into Egypt."[6]

Job likely lived close to Ur, allowing him the opportunity to become educated in Ur's astronomy. Job knew about Bear and Orion constellations and star cluster Pleiades found in Job 9:9. About this verse, Ellicott points out that Job and his countrymen knew astronomy: "His fellow-countrymen had attained to such knowledge of astronomy as is here implied in the specific names of definite constellations."[7]

---

[6] Josephus. Translated by Whiston, *The Works of Flavius Josephus: Antiquities of the* Jews (London: John Bumpus, 1828), 1.8.2, p. 39.

[7] Stanley Leathes, Edited by Charles John Ellicott. *An Old Testament Commentary for English Readers, Vol. IV, Job* (New York: Cassell & Company, 1884), p. 20.

Job knew the stars and constellations. Constellations are stars grouped into recognizable images and given names. Job lists two constellations, Bear and Orion. These two constellations are still some of the most recognizable constellations in the sky. There are 88 named constellations. Some constellations can only be seen in the northern hemisphere, while other constellations can only be seen in the southern hemisphere. Nevertheless, several named constellations can be seen no matter where one looks from the earth into space.

Twelve constellations rank among the most important. They are Aries, Taurus, Gemini, Cancer, Leo, Virgo, Libra, Scorpius, Sagittarius, Capricornus, Aquarius, and Pisces. These 12 constellations form a ring around the earth. From sunset to sunrise, 11 of the 12 constellations can be seen. There is always one constellation that is blocked by the sun at any given moment. The constellation blocked by the sun would mark the time of the year. The sun will move along this path every year. Tracking the sun's movement across these constellations gives the observer knowledge of the time of year. This celestial tracking formed a calendar for early humans. Today, people use calendars that are turned to the correct month. The calendar shows us the exact day of the year to correlate to the earth's location in its rotation around the sun. In the old days, this piece of paper on the wall did not exist; what did exist was the tracking of the sun as it blocked the different constellations throughout the year. The knowledge gleaned from the sun's location within these 12 constellations (just like the calendar today) allowed farmers to know when to do essential activities based on the expected weather. The month of Aries was known to be springtime. By the month of Cancer, it was drier and hotter. In the month of Virgo, crops were harvested. Winter came around Capricornus. The rain intensified in the month of Aquarius.

The primary 12 constellations are no different from the months on a calendar. In Modern-day these 12 constellations are commonly referred to as zodiacs. Some people take these 12 constellations and use them for mystical purposes. The misuse does not make these constellations evil. To make them evil would mean we should throw away our calendars as well. The modern-day calendar has days of the week named after Greek gods, but we do not worship Greek gods. The months are references to false gods as well. The month of August was named after Augustine Caesar who was proclaimed a god by the Romans. Having that name on a calendar does not mean we worship him. The calendar indicates where the earth is in its rotation around the sun. Calendars allow us to communicate to others what is planned at that time of year. The 12 constellations are the 12 months of the year used by the patriarchs of the Bible.

The constellation Hydra is a snake that stretches across several constellations. Leviathan of the skies is well-documented in other cultures and understood to be a star constellation that runs the plane's length that the sun appears to rotate on every year. Job describes the pain that he feels after losing everything except for his faith in God. He uses the sky leviathan symbology to describe the pain he feels: "Lo, let that night be barren; let no joyful voice come therein. Let them curse it that curse the day, who are ready to rouse up leviathan" (Job 3:7-8). Regarding the word "leviathan" in Job 3:8, Walter Maunder states, "There is a word used in Scripture to denote a reptilian monster, which appears in one instance at least to refer to this dragon of eclipse, and so to be used in an astronomical sense."[8] Jonathan Kelsey Burr, regarding the Hebrew word used here for leviathan states, "Lexicographers, gives the ground-form of the word as that which wreathes, or gathers itself into folds. Hence one meaning of the word is serpent, since it moves itself forward by folds."[9]

The constellation Hydra is a star cluster that looks like a snake. Hydra stretches out just under the perceived orbital plane of the sun. For several months a year, the sun passes directly over the constellation Hydra.

Leviathan Solar Eclipse

The skies above Job experienced a rare astronomical event. Job lived at the time and location when an annular solar eclipse occurred. This substantial eclipse appears to be referred to by Job as the leviathan that swallowed the sun.

On June 23, 1917 BC, at about 5:30 PM, the sun was next to the Snake constellation of Hydra's mouth when the sun went into an annular solar eclipse. The annular eclipse would have been a total solar eclipse if the moon was closer to the earth. With the moon not blocking all the sun, a ring of fire could be seen over Mesopotamia. The maximum eclipse was centered

---

[8] E. Walter Maunder, *The Astronomy of the Bible: An Elementary Commentary on the Astronomical References of Holy Scripture* (London: T. Sealey Clark, 1908), p. 202.

[9] Jonathan Kelsey Burr, *A Commentary on the Book of Job: Intended for Popular use* (New York: Phillips & Hunt, 1879), p. 39.

Job's Leviathan
Solar Eclipse June 23, 1917 BC.

Solar eclipse next to the constellation
Hydra's mouth.
It appeared as if Hydra ate the sun.

over the city of Ur. The annular eclipse maxed out at 88% but obstructed 96% of all light. When viewing this annular eclipse, it would have appeared as a ring of fire anywhere in Mesopotamia. If the eclipse were viewed west of Mesopotamia, it would have appeared as a crescent, reminiscent of a bite taken out of the sun. All locations in Mesopotamia would have had slightly exposed sun, but most of the sun would have been obstructed by the moon.

The substantial annular eclipse occurred next to the head of the constellation Hydra. On June 23, 1917 BC, all the stars appeared in the sky within one hour after sunset. Job would have been able to verify the sun's location where it was eclipsed by seeing the constellations in the early night sky. The entire length of Hydra's body could be visible except for its head. Since the sun's orbit always goes just over the entire length of the body of Hydra and the only part that was not visible was the head, one would know the eclipse occurred around Hydra's mouth. The annular eclipse appeared as if Hydra had taken a bite out of the sun.

The leviathan's solar eclipse that Job refers to only occurred over Mesopotamia. If one were not around Mesopotamia, the eclipse would lose its magnitude and not resemble what Job described. Job would need to be close to Mesopotamia to appreciate the leviathan eclipse of June 23, 1917 BC. The description of this eclipse reinforces the location and time that Job is believed to have lived.

Job's Account of the Eclipse

Job 3:2-9 – "Job answered and said: Let the day perish wherein I was born, and the night which said, there is a man-child conceived. Let that day be darkness; let not God from above seek for it, neither let the light shine upon it. Let darkness and the shadow of death claim it for their own; let a cloud dwell upon it; let all that maketh black the day terrify it. As for that night, let thick darkness seize upon it: let it not rejoice among the days of the year; let it not come into the number of the months. Lo, let that night be barren; Let no joyful voice come therein. Let them curse it that curse the day, who are ready to rouse up leviathan. Let the stars of the twilight thereof be dark: Let it look for light, but have none; Neither let it behold the eyelids of the morning."

The normal cycle of daylight and darkness was interrupted. Daytime is when the sun is in the sky illuminating the earth. The night is traditionally dark, and the sun is nowhere to be seen. The phrase "Let that day be darkness" implies a time when the sun is supposed to be shining but is not.

The darkness described here is not the usual darkness. Job 3:3-9 addresses darkness nine times in only seven verses:

1. Night
2. Day be darkness
3. Neither let the light shine upon it
4. Darkness
5. Shadow of death

6. Cloud dwell upon it
7. Let all that maketh blackness the day terrify it
8. Night
9. Thick darkness seize upon it

These nine specific statements of darkness within such a short amount of time emphasize the oddity of the event that happened.

Job could have described the eclipse that occurred from early evening to sunset on June 23, 1917 BC. The solar eclipse started about 4:30 PM, with the maximum eclipse around 5:30 PM. The solar eclipse ended about 6:30 PM with sunset around 7:00 PM. Job describes the visual impact of this eclipse on the stars: "Let the stars of the twilight thereof be dark: Let it look for light, but have none; neither let it behold the eyelids of the morning" (Job 3:9). Job describes an evening eclipse where first "the stars of the twilight" are supposed to shine but do not. Then, as the eclipse ended, the sun got brighter as in "neither let it behold the eyelids of the morning," so one would expect to see the morning stars. However, they too do not appear, giving way to the sun's setting for the night.

It is to this that Adam Clark writes, "*Let the stars of the twilight thereof:* the stars of the twilight may here refer to the planets Venus, Jupiter, Mars, and Mercury, as well as to the brighter fixed stars. *Let it look for light:* Here the darkness is represented as waiting for the luster of the evening star, but is disappointed; and then for the aurora or dawn, but equally in vain. He had prayed that its light, the sun, should not shine upon it, and here

18

he prays that its evening star may be totally obscured and that it might never see the dawning of the day."[10]

Job appears to have described the eclipse as a leviathan. Walter Maunder elaborates, "There is a word used in Scripture to denote a reptilian monster, which appears in one instance at least to refer to the dragon of eclipse, and so to be used in an astronomical sense. Job, in his first outburst of grief cursed the day in which he was born, and cried– 'let them curse it that cursed the day, who are ready to rouse up leviathan. Let the stars of the twilight there of the dark let it look for light, but have none; neither let it behold the eyelids of the morning."[11]

An evening eclipse would fit the description given by Job. As the sun started going into an eclipse, the sky got darker, and the evening stars started coming out. After the maximum eclipse was over, the sky grew brighter, causing the morning stars to start coming out. When the noticeable eclipse was over, the sun went below the horizon. The sunset caused the sky to get darker and the morning stars gave way to the night stars. This parallels Job's story, who sees disappointment like the stars who do not know if it is morning or night. This indicates that the eclipse happens in the evening around sunset.

---

[10] Adam Clarke, *The Holy Bible: A Commentary and Critical Notes,* Vol. III, Job to Solomon's Song. (New York: Carlton and Phillips, 1853), p. 32.

[11] Walter Maunder, *The Astronomy of The Bible: An Elementary Commentary on The Astronomical References on Holy Scripture* (London: T. Sealey Clark 1908), p. 202-203.

Conclusion

Job's conversation with God included a solar eclipse that Job witnessed. Historians know Job lived in an area that experienced the annular eclipse at the time he was alive. Job confirms that he saw the solar eclipse with his description of this specific eclipse's unique characteristics: "Let them curse it that curse the day, who are ready to rouse up leviathan. Let the stars of the twilight thereof be dark: Let it look for light, but have none; Neither let it behold the eyelids of the morning" (Job 3:8-9). The event that Job describes matches the eclipse of 1917 BC. Job's description of the leviathan eating the sun around sunset is similar to what would have been witnessed during the annular eclipse of 1917 BC. Seeing the eclipse fulfills all Scripture requirements of the event; not associating the two would be more of a personal bias versus a fact-seeking conclusion.

Symbolic Impact

The symbology that Job uses creates a benchmark for the Bible. Job was the first to introduce symbology associating sadness to the day being dark. Since Job is the oldest book in the Bible, all the other books would have the opportunity to build upon this symbology. This symbology is used several other times in Scripture:

Micah 3:6 – "The sun shall go down upon the prophets, and the day shall be black over them."

Amos 8:3-9 – "The songs of the temple shall be wailings in that day, saith the Lord Jehovah: the dead bodies shall be many; in every place shall they cast them forth with silence... it shall come to pass in that day, saith the Lord Jehovah, that I will cause the sun to go down at noon, and I will darken the earth in the clear day."

Jeremiah 4:22-23 – "For my people are foolish they known me not; they are sottish children, and they have no understanding; they are wise to do evil, but to do good they have no knowledge. I beheld the earth, and lo, it was waste and void; and the heavens, and they had no light."

2

King Solomon's Ten Tribes Torn Away

At the same time that a solar eclipse is recorded over Jerusalem, God is recorded declaring that He will tear away 10 of the 12 tribes from King Solomon's son. This chapter will look at a method God could have used to communicate with King Solomon and the Prophet Ahijah.

Timing

Historians determined the time when King Solomon died as 932/31 BC. That year is found by looking for the date the tribe of Israel split then subtract a year. The tribes split shortly after Rehoboam became king in 931/30 BC. King Solomon's death occurred about one year before the division. Based on this, King Solomon's death would have occurred around 932/31 BC.

The timing of 1 Kings 11:4 is about one year before King Solomon's death. Subtracting one year from his date of death gives the year 933/32 BC. Therefore, the window of time that

God most likely communicated with King Solomon would lie within 933/32 BC.

Location

The location where God most likely communicated with King Solomon is in Jerusalem. The Bible does not indicate that he left Israel's land, so one can conclude he was within the Promised Land. The Bible is also silent about him traveling about Israel, so one could conclude he was at his palace. King Solomon's primary palace would have been the palace King David built in Jerusalem. This is reinforced in 1 Kings 11:42 with the statement, "Solomon reigned in Jerusalem over all Israel."

The Recorded History

The recorded history of the life of King Solomon is robust. The books of Kings and Chronicles are written by someone other than King Solomon and provide two different views of King Solomon's life. Three other books about King Solomon and Israel are stated to have existed but have been lost. In addition, King Solomon wrote many books, some about his own experiences. The compilation of material about King Solomon is impressive and allows for a detailed study of the man.

Kings and Chronicles are the only two books of the Bible that speak of Solomon that he did not write. Two interactions are recorded by a third party regarding God's direct communication. First, in 1 Kings 11:11, it merely states that God told King Solomon that He would tear His kingdom away and give it to King Solomon's servant. The only other message delivered from God was by the Prophet Ahijah to Jeroboam in 1 Kings 11: 30-32. Chronicles recorded nothing of the event, leaving us no other third-party observations.

In 2 Chronicles 9:29, we are told of three books that no longer exist that document the works of Solomon's life. The authors of these lost books are Nathan the prophet, Ahijah the Shilonite, and Iddo the seer, concerning Jeroboam, the son of Nebat.

In addition to these works, King Solomon wrote one more book in his final days. The book of Ecclesiastes walks us through King Solomon's attempt to come to peace with God's judgment. Ecclesiastes is an invaluable source to understanding the events surrounding both King Solomon and Israel. Only Ecclesiastes contains input from King Solomon concerning his final year.

Ecclesiastes is his darkest book. He comes to the realization that all is vanity. By studying Ecclesiastes, one can understand the moment God communicated to King Solomon and the full ramifications of that judgment from King Solomon's perspective.

King Solomon's Story

King Solomon was the wisest and wealthiest king to reign over Israel. King Solomon is credited with writing the book of Proverbs, some of Psalms, the Song of Songs, and Ecclesiastes. In addition to King Solomon's wisdom, he was very wealthy. Several paragraphs within 1 Kings and 2 Chronicles are dedicated solely to his wealth, such as his numerous wives and how he fashioned gold into everyday objects. This is seen in 2

Chronicles 9:22, which states, "King Solomon exceeded all the kings of the earth in riches and wisdom."

Everything was going well in King Solomon's life until the last year of his life. For a calculated thirty-nine years, King Solomon enjoyed prosperity, wealth, and knowledge. Then God communicated with King Solomon in 1 Kings 11:11, "Wherefore Jehovah said unto Solomon, 'Forasmuch as this is done of thee, and thou hast not kept my covenant and my statutes, which I have commanded thee, I will surely tear the kingdom from thee, and will give it to thy servant.'"

The event described within 1 Kings 11:11 is the Lord speaking to Solomon. However, this Scripture does not elaborate on how God appeared to him or if other people witnessed the interaction. The Scripture does not say God appeared only to King Solomon, just that the Lord spoke to Solomon.

God's primary intent was to speak to Solomon, but God also wanted to speak to all of Israel. This fact can be discerned by reading what God said to Solomon: "I will surely tear the Kingdom from thee, and will give it to thy servant." The statement refers to when the tribes of Israel would be taken away and given to Solomon's servant Jeroboam. Since Israel's fate was being decided, it is not unreasonable to think God would include all the people at some level.

The event of God speaking with King Solomon was the backdrop for the Prophet Ahijah to approach King Solomon's servant Jeroboam.

The Bible does not inform us how the Prophet Ahijah knew that God was tearing ten tribes away from King Solomon and giving them to Jeroboam. What is known is that the message was delivered: "Ahijah laid hold of the new garment that was on him, and tore it in twelve pieces. And he said to Jeroboam, 'take thee ten pieces; for thus saith Jehovah, the God of Israel, behold, I will tear the kingdom out of the hand of Solomon, and will give ten tribes to thee but he shall have one tribe, for my servant David's sake and for Jerusalem's sake, the city which I have chosen out of all the tribes of Israel; because that they have forsaken me, and have worshipped Ashtoreth the goddess of the Sidonians, Chemosh the god of Moab, and Milcom the god of the children of Ammon; and they have not walked in my ways, to do that which is right in mine eyes, and to keep my statutes and mine ordinances, as did David his father. Howbeit I will not take the whole kingdom out of his hand; but I will make him prince all the days of his life, for David my servant's sake whom I chose, who kept my commandments and my statutes; but I will take the kingdom out of his son's hand, and will give it unto thee, even ten tribes.'" (1 Kings 11: 30-35).

The Prophet Ahijah knew God was unhappy with King Solomon. Ahijah also knew God was tearing away part of the kingdom and giving it to his servant. The Bible does not specify how Ahijah or anyone else knew this information. Interestingly, King Solomon's servant does not object to staging a rebellion. Solomon was so concerned by the rebellion led by his servant that he sought to kill Jeroboam (1 Kings 11:40). Jeroboam fled to Shishak, king of Egypt, and stayed with him until the death of Solomon. Kings and Chronicles do not provide detailed information regarding the rebellion of Jeroboam against Solomon, just that King Solomon's servant Jeroboam was involved in a rebellion and escaped to Egypt because King Solomon was looking to kill him. Details about how many other

26

people rebelled with Jeroboam are not provided, just that his mother Zeruah rebelled with him.

The Bible is silent about whether King Solomon stopped trying to kill Jeroboam before the end of his life or if he actively sought to kill him up to his death. What is known is that Jeroboam did not return from Egypt until after King Solomon's death, which could imply there was a death warrant out for him or at the least feared for his life up till the time King Solomon died.

King Solomon wrote one last book in his later years which shows his despair due to the event. Nowhere within the books that King Solomon wrote or those written by third parties tell us that King Solomon did or did not repent of the sins that divided Israel.

After these events, King Solomon died in 932/31 BC, and the kingdom divided just as prophesied.

Eclipse

The skies over Jerusalem may hold answers as to how God communicated with King Solomon and Israel. God spoke to King Solomon around a year before the king's death. Seeing that King Solomon died in 932/31 BC, the event would have occurred near this time but not after it. On January 27, 932 BC, a substantial solar eclipse occurred over Jerusalem in the late afternoon hours.

King Solomon's Severed Silver Cord of Water
Solar Eclipse January 27, 932 BC.

The solar eclipse occurred in
the waterfall of the constellation Aquarius.

The substantial solar eclipse of January 27, 932 BC, occurred directly over Jerusalem about one year before King Solomon's death. The solar eclipse maxed out at a magnitude of 94%, occurring at 3:10 PM. On the eclipse day, the sunrise was at 7:05 AM, and sunset was at 5:27 PM, making the daylight's total time 10 hours and 22 minutes. Israel did not calculate time based on a 60-minute hour but instead divided the total amount of sunlight into twelve equal parts resulting in an hour that varied based on the time of year. By dividing 10 hours and 22 minutes into twelve parts, each hour's length was 51.8 minutes. The solar eclipse was at the maximum amplitude around 3:10 PM, being the late ninth hour, which began at 2:45 PM and the early tenth hour which started at 3:36 PM. Seeing that no watches were available, this time is only estimated and people of that time could easily have believed it was the tenth hour of the day. In addition to this, at the eclipse time, Venus was very bright, and Jupiter could be seen. A total of two planets were visible at the eclipse time, but no stars or constellations were visible. The eclipse location was in the constellation of Aquarius, and the sun was in Aquarius' waterfall. Lastly, January 27 is the last day of Israel's tenth month of the year. This year Israel would only have twelve months versus the occasional thirteen. On January 27, 932 BC, ten months of the year are over and two months remain.

King Solomon's Story with Eclipse Perspective

This section is a hypothetical chain of events based on the above facts.

29

On January 27, 932 BC, a substantial solar eclipse occurred directly over King Solomon in Jerusalem. The eclipse occurred at the end of the tenth month with only two months left. The solar eclipse occurred around the tenth hour of the day and appeared to have removed 10/12 of the sun.

The eclipse was witnessed by all Israel and the Prophet Ahijah, who began prophesying about God's desire for Israel. Prophet Ahijah interpreted that the eclipse occurred when 10/12 months of the year are over, in the tenth hour of their twelve-hour day, and he also observed that the solar eclipse removed 10/12 of the sun from the sky.[12] The Prophet Ahijah saw no stars except for two planets during the event. After pondering this event, Ahijah prophesied that just as 10/12 of the months of the year are over, as 10/12 of the sun would not shine after 10/12 hours of the day was gone, so also 10 of the 12 tribes will be torn away from King Solomon's son. The Prophet Ahijah emphasized this by taking his cloak, cutting it into 12 pieces, and then telling Jeroboam to take 10 for himself. The Prophet Ahijah interpreted the sun had two parts left, the day had two hours left, two months of the year remained, and two planets were showing in the sky, so he concluded that two tribes, Judah and Benjamin, would remain under King Solomon's son's rulership's.

King Solomon refused to believe that God would tear away part of the kingdom and give them to Jeroboam. Solomon said, "Consider the work of God: for who can make that straight, which he hath made crooked? In the day of prosperity be joyful, and in the day of adversity consider; yea, God hath appointed

---

[12] **Warning**: looking at the sun without appropriate safety equipment is dangerous and can result in permanent eye damage causing loss of sight.

the one as well as the other, to the end that man should not find out anything that shall be after him. All this have I seen in my days of vanity: there is a righteous man that perisheth in his righteousness, and there is a wicked man that prolongeth his life in his evil-doing" (Ecclesiastes 7:13-15). Looking at the critical points in his statement, God's plan for Israel and Solomon's resistance can be seen.

King Solomon starts with the statement, "Consider the work of God." Hence, he is contemplating a work that God has or will perform. The statement, "For who can make that straight, which he has made crooked?", parallels King Solomon's long years of kingship over Israel only to have God promise to remove it from his family line—or to make crooked.

The Scripture portion saying, "In the day of adversary consider; yea, God has appointed the one as well as the other," parallels the fact that God appointed Solomon to be a king, but now has God appointing "the other," being Jeroboam. The next portion gives us a sense of despair: "Man should not find out anything that shall be after him." God told King Solomon that his servant Jeroboam would become king after him. However, Solomon is attempting to change the future by ordering the death of Jeroboam. His conflict is highlighted in the passage that says, "Man should not find out anything that shall be after him." This is highlighted in 1 Kings 11:40 when King Solomon resisted God and actively tried to kill Jeroboam, the man God had appointed. The final portion of Scripture of note: "There is a righteous man that perisheth in his righteousness, and there is a wicked man that prolongeth his life in his evil-doing." Two people are involved: one that is wise and one that is wicked. One can deduce that King Solomon believes himself to be the just man who perishes in his righteousness; one can equally deduce that Jeroboam is the wicked man who prolongs life in his wickedness. This is not the sign of a man accepting what God said, but rather one fighting against God.

King Solomon witnessed the solar eclipse but insisted it occurred over everyone, not just himself. King Solomon's thoughts on this can be found in Ecclesiastes 2:12-16, "I turned myself to behold wisdom, and madness, and folly: for what can the man do that cometh after the king? Even that which hath been done long ago. Then I saw that wisdom excelleth folly, as far as light excelleth darkness. The wise man's eyes are in his head, and the fool walketh in darkness: and yet I perceived that one event happeneth to them all. Then said I in my heart, as it happeneth to the fool, so will it happen even to me; and why was I then more wise? Then said I in my heart, that this also is vanity. For of the wise man, even as of the fool, there is no remembrance for ever; seeing that in the days to come all will have been long forgotten. And how doth the wise man die even as the fool!"

King Solomon's contemplation on this event leads him to say, "I saw that wisdom excelleth folly, as far as light excelleth darkness. The wise man's eyes are in his head, and the fool walketh in darkness: and yet I perceived that one event happeneth to them all. Then said I in my heart, as it happeneth to the fool, so will it happen even to me." King Solomon compares himself to wisdom walking in the light and Jeroboam to the fool walking in the darkness. This is interesting, seeing that the sun's darkness represents the ten tribes taken away, and the sunlight represents King Solomon's two tribes.

King Solomon then compares his walk in the light as having his eyes where they belong, whereas Jeroboam's eyes are in the eclipse's darkness, hence not using his eyes but rather his emotions. King Solomon's experience is wrapped up with this statement: "And yet I perceived that one event happeneth to them all." King Solomon's own words inform us that this solar eclipse covers not just himself but everyone. Therefore, God was not talking to just him but everyone. King Solomon concluded that if the total solar eclipse occurred over everyone, why would it be a judgment only against him?

King Solomon concludes the book of Ecclesiastes with a quick summary of the last year of his life.

Ecclesiastes 12:1-8 – "Remember also thy Creator in the days of thy youth, before the evil days come, and the years draw nigh, when thou shalt say, I have no pleasure in them; before the sun, and the light, and the moon, and the stars, are darkened, and the clouds return after the rain; in the day when the keepers of the house shall tremble, and the strong men shall bow themselves, and the grinders cease because they are few, and those that look out of the windows shall be darkened, and the doors shall be shut in the street; when the sound of the grinding is low, and one shall rise up at the voice of a bird, and all the daughters of music shall be brought low; yea, they shall be afraid of that which is high, and terrors shall be in the way; and the almond-tree shall blossom, and the grasshopper shall be a burden, and desire shall fail; because man goeth to his everlasting home, and the mourners go about the streets: before the silver cord is severed, or the golden bowl is broken, or the pitcher is broken at the fountain, or the wheel broken at the cistern, and the dust returneth to the earth as it was, and the spirit returneth unto God who gave it. Vanity of vanities, said the Preacher; all is vanity."

Solomon encourages everyone to remember God in the early parts of their life. Then goes on to say, "Before the evil days come, and the years draw nigh, when thou shalt say, 'I have no pleasure in them.'" King Solomon's words imply that his days of trouble came not because of sin but would have happened regardless.

King Solomon then describes "the evil days" as "the sun, and the light, and the moon, and the stars, are darkened." The description of the sun, light, moon, and stars growing dark referred to the solar eclipse. The eclipse caused the sun to be 10/12 blocked, the light was 10/12 dimmer than its normal strength, the moon was nowhere to be seen as it was blocking the sun, and the only stars visible were Venus and Jupiter.

The impact of the solar eclipse is described: "When the keepers of the house shall tremble, and the strong men shall bow themselves, and the grinders cease because they are few, and those that look out of the windows shall be darkened, and the doors shall be shut in the street; when the sound of the grinding is low." The trembling keepers could refer to Jeroboam running away to Egypt. With Jeroboam rebelling against King Solomon, he could have inspired others to rebel as well. Indeed, King Solomon informs us that all work ceased and no one was moving about. It is unclear whether Israel is hiding in place or left, possibly with Jeroboam.

King Solomon then describes the time of year: "The almond-tree shall blossom, and the grasshopper shall be a burden, and desire shall fail." The season is described in this statement. The almond tree blossoms between early January and late February. At the same time, January to February is when grasshoppers are known to migrate through the territory.

King Solomon describes the solar eclipse by saying, "The silver cord is severed, or the golden bowl is broken, or the pitcher is broken at the fountain, or the wheel broken at the cistern." The month of Aquarius occurs around January to February and is represented by a constellation representing a person with a big bowl pouring water out. The month of Aquarius is the year's rainiest time; therefore, rain is associated with the constellation. The symbology of Aquarius pouring out this life-giving waterfall—represented in a line of over 20 stars—could be described as a silver cord. The solar eclipse covering King Solomon occurred during the month of Aquarius within the water falling from the golden bowl. The solar eclipse within the constellation's waterfall is described as a severed silver cord of water poured from a golden bowl.

King Solomon expresses his frustration with this solar eclipse, "Vanity of vanities, said the Preacher; all is vanity!"

Conclusion

At the same time that a solar eclipse is recorded over Jerusalem, God is recorded declaring that He will be tearing away 10 of the 12 tribes from King Solomon's son.

God's statement occurred within the last year of King Solomon's life. King Solomon died around 932/31 BC; therefore, God's proclamation must have occurred around early 932 BC. The solar eclipse fulfilled the event requirements laid out in Scripture. It is a fact that this eclipse occurred. Therefore, one can say that no other action on God's part is required. God could have chosen to do more but insisting that God had to do more would be wishful thinking driven more on emotion than scriptural necessity.

3

Deborah's Stars Fought

God's prophetic battle in the stars paved the way for Israel's fight against their oppressors. "From heaven fought the stars, from their courses they fought against Sisera" (Judges 5:20). Deborah witnessed the solar eclipse that occurred around the head of the constellation Scorpius. This war in the stars with the archer killing the scorpion is paralleled with the killing of Israel's enemy General Sisera with a stake to his head.

Deborah's knowledge of God's plan brought victory over Israel's oppressors. Many have contemplated how Deborah received this knowledge from God. MacLaren's Expositions proposed, "There may be some trace of ancient astrological notions."[13] MacLaren's note may have found the method of how God communed with Deborah.

---

[13] Alexander Maclaren, *Expositions of Holy Scripture: The Book of Judges,* (London: Hodder and Stoughton) p. 209.

This chapter will examine Deborah and Barak's biblical account in retrospect of a rare solar eclipse that occurred in the sky over Israel.

Year Timing

The timing for the book of Judges started after the division of the Promised Land by Joshua and ended with the Prophet Samuel. Historians believe the timing for Deborah and Barak's story occurred between 1250 BC and 1150 BC.

Season Timing

Israel's battle under Deborah and Barak is thought to have occurred during the rainy season. Two verses allude to large sums of rainfall:

1. **Judges 5:4** – "The earth trembled, the heavens also dropped, Yea, the clouds dropped water."
2. **Judges 5:21** – "The river Kishon swept them away."

Either the two stated verses or some lost traditions may have influenced Josephus' recorded account of the battle that Deborah and Barak fought when he said, "Deborah retained them, and commanded them to fight the enemy that very day, for that they should conquer them, and God would be their assistance. So the battle began; and when they were come to a close fight, there came down from heaven a great storm, with a vast quantity of rain and hail, and the wind blew the rain in the face of the Canaanites, and so darkened their eyes, that their arrows and slings were of no advantage to them, nor would the coldness of the air permit the soldiers to make use of their swords; while this storm did not so much incommode the Israelites, because it came in their backs."[14] Josephus' recorded account would appear to have placed the battle during the cold, rainy time of year.

Location

The prophesied battle location and the encampment of Sisera is called Harosheth Haggoyim, located next to the Kishon River within the Megiddo valley. Easton described this location in his Bible Dictionary as a "place of troops, originally one of the royal cities of the Canaanites (Josh. 12:21), belonged to the tribe of Manasseh (Judg. 1:27), but does not seem to have been fully occupied by the Israelites till the time of Solomon (1 Kings 4:12; 9:15). The valley or plain of Megiddo was part of the plain of Esdraelon, the great battlefield of Palestine. It was here Barak gained a notable victory over Jabin, the King of Hazor, whose general, Sisera, led on the hostile army. Barak rallied the warriors of the northern tribes, and under the encouragement of Deborah, the prophetess, attacked the Canaanites in the great plain. The army of Sisera was thrown into complete confusion, and was engulfed in the waters of the Kishon, which had risen and overflowed its banks (Judg. 4:5)."[15] In further reference to the river, he stated, "When the Kishon was at its height, it would

---

[14] Josephus, Translated by Whiston, *The Works of Flavius Josephus: Antiquities of the Jews* (London: John Bumpus, 1828), 5.5.3-4, p. 141.

[15] M. G. Easton, *Illustrated Bible Dictionary* (New York: Harper and Brothers, 1893), p. 454.

be, partly on account of its quicksand, as impassable as the ocean itself to a retreating army."[16]

Easton pointed out that the River Kishon is quicksand most of the year, but it becomes a flowing river that could overflow its banks during the rainy season. Location facts reinforce the conclusion that this battle must have been fought during the rainy season, since "the river Kishon swept them away" (Judges 5:21). This is only possible with lots of rain.

Deborah lived within the tribe of Ephraim. Judges 4:5 says, "She dwelt under the palm-tree of Deborah between Ramah and Beth-el in the hill-country of Ephraim: and the children of Israel came up to her for judgment." The location for "the palm-tree of Deborah" is between 5 and 12 miles north of Jerusalem and southeast of the battlefield.

Barak lived in Kedesh within the tribe of Naphtali (Judges 4:6). Kedesh is located northeast of the battlefield.

Deborah's Story

The story of Deborah consists of two chapters found in Judges 4 and 5. Judges 4 is a literal telling of Israel's sufferings from the twenty years of oppression through the victory over their oppressor Sisera. Judges chapter 5 is a poetic retelling of Judges 4. Comparing both chapters will shed light on the actual events.

After 20 years of oppression by King Jabin of the Canaanites, Deborah received a prophesy of Israel while under a palm tree. The prophesy was of a battle that Israel would win over their

---

[16] Ibid, p. 411.

oppressor. Barak was summoned to Deborah so that the battle plan prophesy could be executed. Barak was directed to take 10,000 men to Mount Tabor.

The Canaanite Sisera was the head general of King Jabin's army. When Sisera received word of the 10,000-man Israelite army, he gathered a massive army to stop it, one that included chariots.

The battle is summed up in Judges 5:20-21, "From heaven fought the stars, from their courses they fought against Sisera. The river Kishon swept them away, that ancient river, the river Kishon. O my soul, march on with strength."

Sisera's large army and the chariots were swept away in the river Kishon. Sisera ran away from his military and ended up at Jael's tent in hopes of hiding from Israel. Sisera's safety in the tent was short-lived when Jael drove a nail through his head.

Eclipse

The skies above Deborah experienced a rare astronomical event. Deborah lived at the time and location when a solar eclipse occurred. This substantial eclipse appears to be referred to by Deborah as "the stars fought."

At Deborah's location and time, the stars fought at 4:45 PM on October 30, 1207 BC. The sun was located on the head of the constellation Scorpius. The sun was eclipsed by the moon, resulting in a 91% eclipse visible at the palm tree of Deborah. The eclipsed sun would have blocked out 91% of the daytime light, reducing visibility to that of twilight hours.

Deborah's Stars Fought
Solar Eclipse October 30, 1207 BC.

Sagittarius is the top constellation.
Scorpio is the bottom constellation.
At sunset, Scorpio is swept under the horizon.

The wind would have started blowing as a result of the eclipse. The event in the sky gave the appearance that the constellations were fighting.

Two constellations in the area of the eclipse are Sagittarius and Scorpius. Joseph A. Seiss states the following about the two Constellations:

"**SCORPIO**, the Scorpion: the figure of a gigantic, noxious, and deadly insect, with its tail and sting uplifted in anger, as if striking."

"**SAGITTARIUS**, the Bowman: the figure of a horse with the body, arms, and head of a man — a centaur — with a drawn bow and arrow pointed at the Scorpion."[17] Moreover, he states, "In all tongues he is named, as in our charts, the Archer, the Bowman, He who sends forth the arrow. In form he is the Centaur, the Piercer."[18]

Sagittarius stands over Scorpius with a bow and arrow drawn and pointed at it. The eclipsed sun was located on the head of the scorpion constellation and would have appeared to be a death blow by Sagittarius the next constellation over. The eclipse would appear to have been a celestial battle of the constellations with only one survivor.

---

[17] Joseph A. Seiss, Gospel in the Stars: Or, Primeval Astronomy (New York: Charles C. Cook, 1910), p. 42.

[18] Ibid, p. 140.

One hour after the solar eclipse, the constellation Scorpius is swept under the earth's horizon, and the constellation Sagittarius would be standing victoriously visible in the early night sky.

Deborah's Story with Eclipse Perspective

This section is a hypothetical story based on the above facts.

After 20 years of oppression, Israel's third Judge received guidance from God. Deborah witnessed the stars fighting at 4:45 PM on October 30, 1207 BC. The constellation Scorpius had the sun located on its head. About one hour before sunset, the sun became eclipsed by the moon, resulting in a 91% eclipse. Deborah knew the constellations Sagittarius had a celestial arrow pointed at Scorpius's head. Deborah believed the arrow was released and delivered a fatal blow to the scorpion. This attack is represented by the solar eclipse occurring on the scorpion's head. Deborah then noticed that the now-dead Scorpion constellation completely disappeared, swept away by the horizon, leaving the Sagittarius constellation fully visible in the night sky as the battle champion.

Deborah paralleled this celestial fight to Israel's battle against Sisera. Deborah believed that the Archer constellation Sagittarius represented Israel, and the constellation Scorpius represented their enemy Sisera. Deborah interpreted this cosmic battle to mean that Israel was to go to battle against Sisera. The battle would result in Sisera's defeat and death, being fatally impaled in the head, represented by the sun's eclipse on the scorpion's head. Further, Deborah prophesied that Sisera's army would be swept down the river, symbolized by the constellation being swept out of the sky at sunset. Finally, Deborah prophesied that Israel would be victorious after seeing the constellation representing Israel was observable in the night sky.

Deborah summoned Barak and informed him that God fought from the heavens (Judges 5:20), "From heaven fought the stars, from their courses they fought against Sisera." Barak believed Deborah but did not have the knowledge to understand the stars, resulting in Barak's hesitation to go without Deborah.

Adam Clarke stated, "the Septuagint made a remarkable addition to the speech of Barak: 'If thou wilt go with me I will go; but if thou wilt not go with me, I will not go; because I know not the day in which the Lord will send his angel to give me success.' By which he appears to mean, that although he was certain of a divine call to this work, yet, as he knew not the time in which it would be proper for him to make the attack, he wished that Deborah, on whom the Divine Spirit constantly rested, would accompany him to let him know when to strike that blow, which he knew would be decisive."[19]

The Septuagint notation of "the Lord will send his angel to give me success" indicates that this angel would most likely be the angel Deborah saw fighting in the stars represented by the constellation Sagittarius. The prophetic battle occurred at 4:45 PM on October 30, 1207 BC, and now the angel warrior will come down to earth to fulfill the prophecy.

---

[19] Adam Clarke, *The Holy Bible: A Commentary and Critical Notes, Vol. II, Joshua to Esther* (New York: Lane & Sandford, 1842), p. 117.

Barak did not understand the event in the sky at 4:45 PM on October 30, 1207 BC. Barak concluded that he would need Deborah to come with him to decipher the will of God. Deborah went with Barak and was able to assist with the relaying of God's will to Barak.

When the time was correct, Deborah told Barak the day the Lord had chosen was now, for God had gone out before them, demonstrated in the earlier eclipse. Judges 4:14 says, "And Deborah said unto Barak, Up; for this is the day in which Jehovah hath delivered Sisera into thy hand; is not Jehovah gone out before thee? So Barak went down from mount Tabor, and ten thousand men after him."

Deborah's celestial vision ended with Scorpio's death and subsequential sweeping away by the earth's horizon, so also on earth, Sisera's army was washed away by the river just as Deborah prophesied. The fact that this river was flowing indicates that the battle occurred in the year's rainy season. With the eclipse calling Judah to the war on October 30, the battle probably occurred from December to January. The river flowing and eclipse in the late fall give strength to each other.

Sisera died the same way the Scorpion constellation died in the celestial war. The scorpion constellation died with Sagittarius shooting an arrow into Scorpio's head, symbolized by the solar eclipse on Scorpio's head. The earthly battle unfolded the same way the celestial battle did. Sisera was impaled by a tent stake to the head just as the scorpion took an arrow to the head in the prophecy. Sisera's army was then swept away by the river just as Scorpio in the heavens was swept away by the earth's horizon.

Deborah's poem of the events concludes with the observation, "So let all thine enemies perish, O Jehovah: But let them that love him be as the sun when he goeth forth in his might. And the land had rest forty years" (Judges 5:31). Deborah associated the sun going dim during the solar eclipse with Sisera's symbolic death. Deborah continued by comparing Israel's renewed life in the unobstructed sunlight.

Conclusion

God's prophetic battle in the stars paved the way for Israel's fight against their oppressors. Deborah witnessed the Solar eclipse that occurred around the head of the constellation Scorpius. Judge Deborah witnessed the stars fighting in the events on October 30, 1207 BC. "From heaven fought the stars, from their courses they fought against Sisera" (Judges 5:20). This war in the stars with the archer killing the scorpion is paralleled with the killing of Israel's enemy General Sisera with a stake to his head. Since the solar eclipse of October 30, 1207 BC, fulfills all the scriptural requirements for the moment God spoke to Deborah, the only reason for mandating another miracle would be personal desire.

4

Gideon's Trumpet of God

G ideon's story provides an insight into the impact that a solar eclipse can have on the immediate community and the long-term shaping of Bible symbology.

Gideon went from being the least of his tribe to one of the most outstanding judges when God clothed him in the Spirit and blew the trumpet. At that time a rare natural phenomenon occurred in the skies that could give insight into everyone's reaction in Ophrah and the future symbolic impact on Scripture.

Location

Gideon's story most likely takes place within the land promised to the tribe of Manasseh west of the Jordan River. Gideon was living with his father Joash in the city of Ophrah when God communed with him, as noted in Judges 6:11. A city by the name of Ophrah is located inside the land given to the tribe of Benjamin. It is widely believed by historians not to be the same town that Gideon lived in since he was of the tribe of Manasseh. The location of Gideon's Oprah is not known but believed to be located within the land granted to the Manasseh tribe west of the Jordan River. The West Manasseh land started in the southeast, just above the land given to the tribe of Benjamin next to the Jordan river and extended as far northwest to Mount Carmel next to the Mediterranean Sea.

The second location of interest is where Gideon attacked the Midians. The battle's location is believed to have occurred in the valley of Megiddo located inside the land belonging to the Manasseh tribe living west of the Jordan River.

Timing

The judgeship of Gideon started shortly after Deborah's judgeship ended. Deborah began judging in 1207 BC and lasted forty years. During which time, Israel did as God commanded and Israel lived in peace. After the death of Deborah, Israel returned to their sinful ways. The sin resulted in the Midianites' oppression over Israel for seven years. Deborah judged Israel for 40 years from 1207 BC to 1167 BC followed by an undisclosed length of time when Israel sinned. The duration of this sin when added to the seven years of oppression would give us the date when Gideon began his judgeship.

Deborah's solar eclipse was in 1207 BC, and Gideon's solar eclipse was in 1157 BC, a difference of fifty years. The length of time that Israel sinned is not given in the Bible, but if that length of time is three years and added to the forty-seven years, it gives the total of fifty years. The two eclipses witnessed first by Deborah and then by Gideon appear to fit the Bible's timeline, strengthening the fact that the event happened as stated and demonstrating the date's viability.

The time of year when the Holy Spirit covered Gideon took place in summer. It was "when Israel had sown, that the Midianites came up, and the Amalekites, and the children of the east; they came up against them" (Judges 6:3). The verse mentions the harvest, and the typical window of time for the harvest is summer. The harvesting time is between May and July, depending on the weather. Seeing that the harvest was grown and ripe for the picking indicates it was about this time of the year. The time of year is indicated when the angel approached Gideon and encouraged him to destroy the altar. The Scripture informs us Gideon was threshing wheat; therefore, it must have been summer.

Gideon's Story

After the Judgeship of Deborah, the tribes of Israel began worshiping false gods. Because of Israel's sins, God allowed the Midianites to oppress Israel for seven years (Judges 6:1-10). Every year, when the time for harvest arrived, the Midianites would descend on Israel and take everything, whether it be grain or livestock. Israel's self-preservation drove them into the mountains where they hewed caves to conceal themselves from the Midianites. The oppression continued as long as Israel pursued false gods.

Gideon's family lived in fear of the Midianites. Unlike most Israelites, Gideon's family did not hide in a cave but a house in Ophrah. Even though Gideon's family lived in the city, they still feared the Midianites. Gideon's fear can be seen in how he concealed himself in the winepress and referred to himself as "my family is the poorest in Manasseh, and I am the least in my father's house." Gideon could not see himself being the one to unite Israel under God and end the oppression of the Midianites.

Gideon's father had an altar erected to Baal. After several reassurances from the angel of the Lord, Gideon tore down his father's altar and wooden image to the god Baal. Gideon then made an altar to Israel's God and sacrificed two bulls on it. Gideon's new altar and sacrifice were in direct conflict with the Israelites' Baal worship.

The Baal worshipers saw the second bull being burned as a burnt offering in the morning and became angry. They demanded that Gideon be turned over to be killed. Gideon's father refused to turn him over (Judges 6:25-32). Gideon's father rationalized with the Israelites that were standing up for the false god Baal. Gideon's father's fast thinking subdued the angry mob. Gideon was then given the nickname "Jerubbaal."

Then the Spirit of the Lord moved over Gideon and the tribes of Israel. The Holy Spirit clothed Gideon, and He blew the trumpet. The Spirit's movement was so powerful that the Israelites who worshiped the false god Baal repented and united behind Gideon. Israel rallied behind Gideon after the Holy Spirit moved, and the Midianites became terrified. God chose to deliver Israel through the primary use of one man. God's endorsement of Gideon had three primary parts, as noted in Judges 6:34, "The Spirit of Jehovah came upon Gideon; and He blew a trumpet; and Abiezer was gathered together after him."

First, the Scripture informs us that the Spirit of the Lord came upon Gideon. The way it is translated here implies the Holy Spirit was present but no more. The translated word "came" is the Hebrew Strong's word 3847, "labesh," which means "to put on a garment or clothe"[20] as noted in Strong's Concordance. Two popular commentaries agree:

> ***The Cambridge Bible for Schools and Colleges*** — "The spirit of the Lord came upon— Rather, clothed." [21]
>
> ***Wesley's Explanatory Notes*** — "The Hebrew is, The Spirit of the Lord clothed Gideon; clothed him as a robe, to put honor upon him; clothed him as a coat of mail to put a defense upon him."[22]

The word *labesh* informs us how this weak person became strong, because Gideon now has God present in the form of the Holy Spirit upon him.

The translation of *labesh* being "clothed" makes more sense considering Gideon's downfall with the ephod. After Gideon subdued the Midianites, Israel asked him to rule over them, but he refused. Gideon then asked for gold and purple fabric that was taken from the dead Midianites. The materials were then used to make an ephod:

> **Judges 8:24-27** – "Gideon said unto them, I would make a request of you, that ye would give me every man the ear-rings of his spoil. (For they had golden ear-rings,

---

[20] James Strong, *Dictionaries of the Hebrew and Greek Words* (New York: Eaton & Mains, 1890) p. 58.

[21] J. J. Lias, *The Cambridge Bible for Schools and Colleges* (Cambridge: University Press, 1884), p. 108.

[22] John Wesley, *Explanatory Notes, 1754-1765.*

because they were Ishmaelites.) And they answered, we will willingly give them. And they spread a garment, and did cast therein every man the earrings of his spoil. And the weight of the golden earrings that he requested was a thousand and seven hundred shekels of gold; beside the crescents, and the pendants, and the purple raiment that was on the kings of Midian, and beside the chains that were about their camels' necks. And Gideon made an ephod thereof, and put it in his city, even in Ophrah: and all Israel played the harlot after it there; and to his house."

The ephod was a holy garment that God commanded Moses to make. The ephod was an embroidered garment with gold and purple fabric. The embroidered ephod is the holy garment that a priest of the Lord wore. The holy garment's construction for Aaron as the first high priest is described thus:

Exodus 28:5-14 – "And they shall take the gold, and the blue, and the purple, and the scarlet, and the fine linen. And they shall make the Ephod of gold, of blue, and purple, scarlet, and fine twined linen, the work of the skillful workman. It shall have the two shoulder-pieces joined to the two ends thereof, that it may be joined together. And the skillfully woven band, which is upon it, wherewith to gird it on, shall be like the work thereof and of the same piece; of gold, of blue, and purple, and scarlet, and fine twined linen. And thou shalt take two onyx stones, and grave on them the names of the children of Israel: Six of their names on the one stone, and the names of the six that remain on the other stone, according to their birth. With the work of an engraver in stone, like the engravings of a signet, shalt thou engrave the two stones, according to the names of the children of Israel: thou shalt make them to be enclosed in settings of gold. And thou shalt put the two stones upon the shoulder-pieces of the Ephod, to be stones of memorial for the children of Israel: and Aaron shall bear their names before Jehovah upon his two shoulders for a memorial. And thou shalt make settings of gold, and two chains of pure gold; like cords shalt thou make them, of wreathen work: and thou shalt put the wreathen chains on the settings."

The embroidered ephod was a holy garment to be worn only by the high priest. Gideon was not the high priest; he could not even be *a* priest seeing that he was of Manasseh's tribe instead of Levi's. This may be why the Bible does not tell us that Gideon put the ephod on, only that Gideon put it on display in his hometown of Ophrah.

Gideon's ephod gives us further clarity into the statement, "The Spirit of Jehovah (clothed) Gideon." Gideon could have done anything with his money, but he chose to make the ephod. His reasoning for doing this is not given, but since he did not put it on, it does not appear that he was attempting to become the high priest. A probable reason for the ephod's construction was as a relic. This indicates that Gideon compares his experience of being covered by the Lord's Spirit to a new high priest clothed in the ephod. If considered a souvenir or relic, it is easy to see how all Israel would come to see it on display and play the harlot with it.

The second part of the Holy Spirit's presence is seen when "He blew a trumpet." This is reminiscent of Numbers 10:9 when Moses gave directions for sounding the trumpets. He said, "When ye go to war in your land against the adversary that oppresses you, then ye shall sound an alarm with the trumpets; and ye shall be remembered before Jehovah your God, and ye shall be saved from your enemies." The sounding of this trumpet was so moving that it inspired the Abiezers to follow the "poorest in Manasseh" and "the least in my father's house." The actions of the Spirit coming upon Gideon and the trumpets sounding were moving. Thousands of the house of his tribe returned to the God of Israel and came to assist Gideon. It is incredible to see the entire tribe suddenly shift from following false gods to seeking the God of Israel. One should ask what event would drive such a change in attitude.

The third evidence of the Holy Spirit's presence was that the "Abiezer was gathered together after him."

The Midianites oppressed Israel for seven years. During the seven years of oppression, the Abiezrites and all of Israel pursued false gods and preserved their lives by hiding. The Bible informs us that only Gideon stood up to Israel's Baal worshipers by destroying the false altar and only Gideon's father attempted to protect Gideon from them.

The Abiezrites abandonment of Baal worship to rally behind Gideon is proof that the Holy Spirit moved them. With the seven-year history of pacification and Baal worship, the uprising of all Israel against the Midianites is entirely out of character and completely unexpected. The unification of Israel must have been orchestrated by the Holy Spirit and not man.

The statement in Judges 6:34 that "the Spirit of Jehovah came upon Gideon; and he blew a trumpet; and Abiezer was gathered together after him" implies that God blew the trumpet, not Gideon. This verse is reminiscent of the final arrival of Jesus mentioned in 1 Corinthians 15:51-54, "Behold! I tell you a mystery: We all shall not sleep, but we shall all be changed, in a moment, in the twinkling of an eye, at the last trumpet: for the trumpet shall sound, and the dead shall be raised incorruptible, and we shall be changed. For this corruptible must put on incorruption, and this mortal shall have put on immortality." The trumpet will be sounded not by man but by God, and the new body is from God as well. Jesus is to arrive with the sound of a trumpet, and the chosen will be clothed in imperishable new clothing. There are parallels between 1 Corinthians 15:51 and Judges 6:34. In both events, God blew the trumpet and clothed the chosen. The Abiezrites would have witnessed an event, and when told that it was because of God choosing Gideon, it struck a chord with all of Israel. This event moved Israel into full action.

Eclipse

One extraordinary event in the twelfth century BC is a near-total solar eclipse in the year 1157 BC.

The eclipse covered the entire land inherited by the Manasseh tribe living west of the Jordan River. The solar eclipse began on August 19, 1157 BC, around 7:30 AM. At 8:40 AM, the sun became 100% eclipsed in lower Israel. At the same time, the southern portions of Western Manasseh were around 99% eclipsed. The eclipse magnitude decreased the further north one goes. The magnitude of the eclipse was 97% in Megiddo and

96% at Mount Carmel, being the furthest north point of Western Manasseh. The southern region of Manasseh potentially could have a viewing of the sun's corona and the phenomenon called Baily's beads. All the land of western Manasseh had a sun with a dominant dark circle inside it.

Thousands of crescent-shaped images appeared under the trees. The images are identical to the event in the sky; as the eclipse advances, the images on the ground change. The later stages of the eclipse could be viewed through this use of pinhole images.

All of Manasseh witnessed a substantial loss of sunlight when the sun experienced a near-total solar eclipse for about three minutes. A cool breeze would have rushed in as the sky became dark. In the southernmost parts of Manasseh, the eclipse would have lines of light similar to spokes on a bike tire radiating outward from the dark circle in the center. The rest of Manasseh would have seen a crescent-shaped sliver of the sun with the sun's center being a black circle.

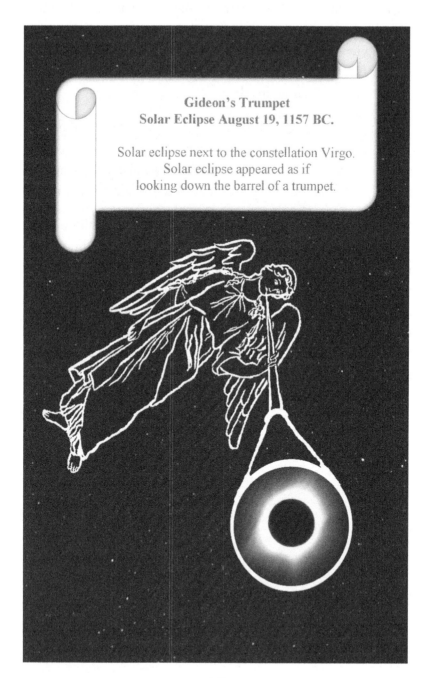

Gideon's Trumpet
Solar Eclipse August 19, 1157 BC.

Solar eclipse next to the constellation Virgo.
Solar eclipse appeared as if
looking down the barrel of a trumpet.

The inhabitants of Manasseh would be able to view the eclipse two ways. First, they could view the eclipse as pinhole images under trees. The second way was to look directly at the sun. (Looking at the sun with approved glasses is the most popular option today. I use ISO 12312-2 rated viewing glasses to view the sun safely because looking directly at the sun can result in permanent eye damage and loss of sight.)[23] At the time of Gideon, they did not have these glasses, so people may have chosen to look directly at the sun.

On July 16, 1330 AD, Taddeo Gaddi did this during the partial eclipse over Florence, Italy. Taddeo Gaddi stared at the solar eclipse that maxed out at 90%. The eclipse damaged his eyes, leaving him with permanent vision degradation. Being a professional painter, Taddeo Gaddi began incorporating the solar eclipse that he witnessed into his artwork. One of his most famous paintings, titled *Annunciation to the Shepherds,* incorporates this solar eclipse. The painting has two shepherds, a sheepdog and several sheep in it. Everyone is looking away from a solar eclipse except one shepherd that is looking directly at it. The solar eclipse is depicted as a crescent of the sun around the head of an angel. While staring at the eclipse, Taddeo Gaddi noticed a bright crescent shape of the sun due to a circular object blocking the sun. Today we know this circular object was the moon, but Gaddi appears to have associated this dark circular object with an angel. After witnessing this eclipse, Taddeo Gaddi's paintings became synonymous with these halos that he began placing over all the heads of godly people. Taddeo Gaddi

---

[23] **Warning***: looking at the sun without appropriate safety equipment is dangerous and can result in permanent eye damage causing loss of sight.*

witnessed a 90% eclipse and associated the bright crescent around a dark center with a halo around the head of an angel.

Similarly, Gideon witnessed a 97% to 99% solar eclipse and associated the bright crescent around a dark center with the end of a trumpet. The eclipse was not just for Gideon. It would have been a moving experience for the entire tribe.

Gideon's Story with Eclipse Perspective

This section is a hypothetical story based on the above facts.

Gideon witnessed great atrocities toward God with the worship of idols and sacrifices in the name of Baal. Gideon was convinced that the worship of false gods was a sin. Gideon also knew standing up to the Baal Worshipers would result in death. In a depth of despair, an angel appeared to Gideon and assured him that God would protect him if he followed God. Gideon destroyed the sacred site of Baal with complete trust in God and constructed an altar to the true God in its place.

The following morning, the village noticed the altar to Baal had been torn down, and a bull was being offered as a burnt offering in its place. The action was so offensive to the Baal worshipers that they demanded Gideon be turned over to be killed. Gideon's father was the only person to defend him. Gideon's father convinced the Baal worshipers to let Baal defend himself. The angry mob disassembled after giving Gideon the nickname "Jerubbaal, saying, let Baal contend against him."

At this crucial moment in time, the Lord spoke. On August 19, 1157 BC, God sent the total solar eclipse directly over Gideon, his tribe, and the Baal worshipers. During this event, a circle of blackness moved across Southern Israel. As the moon blocked out 90% of the light, a strong breeze would have rushed past Gideon and all of Manasseh.

The sunlight's full strength disintegrated within one hour, leaving only 3% to 1% of the standard light. Gideon felt God's presence covering him in the darkness, reminiscent of the high priest putting on the ephod for the first time. As the darkness covered Gideon, he would have felt the Holy Spirit covering him like a holy garment of empowerment and strength. In the sky over the southernmost parts of Manasseh, the moon blocked out the sun, leaving a dark center with the sun's corona radiating outward. The other parts of Manasseh experienced the moon blocking most of the light, leaving a thin crescent of the sun. All locations in Manasseh would have experienced a 99% to 96% cover of darkness over the land. All of Manasseh would see a dark hole where the sun should be, giving the appearance of looking into a trumpet. The eclipse caused the Israelites who worshiped Baal to scream. The sorrowful screaming would have appeared to be God's trumpet being blown in the heavens, calling His lost children back to Him and preparing them for battle. The eclipse caused the Israelites to abandon their false god Baal and return to the true God. Israel was whole again and emboldened to end their oppression.

At the time of the eclipse, the Midianites were gathering for their yearly raids on Israel. The Midianites would have been terrified by the eclipse. The near-total solar eclipse would have been seen as an omen of disaster for the aggressive Midianites. Walter Maunder, in his book, *The Astronomy of The Bible*, summarizes what people 3000 years ago must have felt when witnessing a total solar eclipse: "The unspeakable terror such an event must have caused in ages long ago, when it came utterly unforeseen, and it was impossible to understand what was really taking place? And so, in the olden time, an eclipse of the sun came as an omen of terrible disaster, nay as being itself one of the worst of disasters. It came so to all nations but one. But to that nation the word of the prophet had come."[24] The Midianites could have been so terrified that they could have begun screaming in pure terror. The sound of screaming combined with a trumpet's appearance in the sky could have inspired the description of the near-total solar eclipse as a trumpet being blown by God.

Gideon and his tribe saw the eclipse differently than the Midianites. Gideon saw it as an endorsement by God that he was doing the right thing and that God had transformed him into a new leader for Israel in the time of their oppression. In the eclipse's aftermath, Gideon's tribe, the Abiezrites, rallied around Gideon, and he sent messengers to the surrounding areas. All the locations that Gideon sent his messengers had witnessed the sun at 95% to 99% eclipsed. The messengers likely informed them of Gideon's confrontation with Baal worshipers and the subsequent near-total solar eclipse over Gideon. Gideon and his messengers appeared to have associated this near-total solar eclipse with God blowing His trumpet. The solar eclipse brought back Israel's lost to the worship of God and assembled an army to fight the Midianites.

---

[24] E. Walter Maunder, *The Astronomy of the Bible: An Elementary Commentary on the Astronomical References of Holy Scripture* (London: T. Sealey Clark & Co., 1907) p. 119.

This can be seen in the fact that 32,000 people rallied to Gideon, and of that, 22,000 were fearful and afraid.

The Midianites would have seen the 32,000 Israelites coming to Gideon's side. The sight of so many people uprising must have been terrifying for the Midianites. This is seen in the dream that a Midianite had:

Judges 7:13-15 – "There was a man telling a dream unto his fellow; and he said, Behold, I dreamed a dream; and, lo, a cake of barley bread tumbled into the camp of Midian, and came unto the tent, and smote it so that it fell, and turned it upside down, so that the tent lay flat. And his fellow answered and said, this is nothing else save the sword of Gideon the son of Joash, a man of Israel: into his hand God hath delivered Midian, and all the host. And it was so, when Gideon heard the telling of the dream, and the interpretation thereof, that he worshipped; and returned into the camp of Israel, and said, arise; for Jehovah hath delivered into your hand the host of Midian."

The Midianites were terrified of Israel. The Midianites' numbers were so large that the Bible states they were as "like locus for multitude; and their camels were without number" (Judges 7:12). Even in their vast numbers, they feared Israel as a Midianite warrior stated, "This is nothing else save the sword of Gideon the son of Joash, a man of Israel: into his hand God hath delivered Midian, and all the host." The fear of Israel by the Midianites was a new thing, primarily since they had gathered to raid Israel. Now they fear Gideon and Israel. The solar eclipse with the subsequent rallying of 32,000 Israelites around Gideon caused a heart change in all the Midianites.

The trumpet's sounding was so effective that timid people mustered up enough courage to go and meet the enemy. Remember, the tribes of Israel were so scared that they would rather hide in caves, but they came running to Gideon after the sounding of the trumpet.

Gideon realized that numbers do not win wars. Large armies such as the opposing Midianites had appeared unstoppable. The fact is, unless the large group is highly trained, equipped, and dedicated, the numbers are more of a disadvantage than an advantage. Gideon sent home 22,000 who were fearful and afraid. Gideon then selected only 300 men for the battle against the Midianites, a more manageable number to command on the battlefield. The Midianites, however, would have assumed that all 32,000 were attacking! The result was that the Midianites fell into a frenzy and attacked each other.

The concept of armies accidentally attacking them-selves is known as friendly fire. The battlefield is a very complex, fast-moving, adrenalin-filled environment. The accidental killing of fellow soldiers on the battle-field has occurred from the first war ever fought. Today, this is called friendly fire and occurs when a soldier accidentally misidentifies a soldier as an enemy. Friendly fire is a genuine and scary threat on any battlefield, even today.

To avoid friendly fire, the first investment a military traditionally makes is in the soldiers' uniforms. When I joined the military in 1999, the first thing the Air Force did was cut my hair and give me a uniform. I quickly discovered that the uniforms created an instantaneous association with the United States Military. Whenever I noticed the uniform worn by a person, I knew they were a brother or sister in arms, and I could trust them. The rapid identification of the uniform allows soldiers to Identify an ally versus an enemy at a glance.

Gideon used the intel that he gathered from the Midianite soldiers against them. Gideon knew the soldiers were afraid and believed Gideon was going to win. It is likely that the soldiers were not dressed in uniforms but in everyday clothing that looked just like the Israelites' clothes. With the intelligence gathered, Gideon realized the potential to turn the Midianite soldiers against themselves. This is what Gideon did; he waited until the Midianites went to sleep that night and then woke them with an overwhelming sound of war trumpets and mountains full

of torches. The Midianites believed they were being attacked by an army of Israelites, numbering above 32,000 and looked just like themselves. Without a method to distinguish between friend or foe, they began attacking themselves. The battle tactic that Gideon used was brilliant.

Conclusion

It is impressive to see the Israelites abandon the false gods readying themselves for battle after being scared of the Midianites. It is equally impressive to see the Midianite army, already prepared for war, become so afraid. Something amazing happened, and the eclipse's timing directly overhead at that time would have provided such a stimulus. Since the solar eclipse of August 19, 1157 BC, fulfills all the scriptural requirements for the moment God clothed Gideon and blew the trumpet, the only reason for mandating another miracle would be personal desire.

Impact on the Bible

God's blowing of the trumpet became a symbol for God's arrival and subsequent judgment. Note the following verses.

1 Corinthians 15:52 – "In a moment, in the twinkling of an eye, at the last trumpet: for the trumpet shall sound, and the dead shall be raised incorruptible, and we shall be changed."

1 Thessalonians 4:16 – "For the Lord himself shall descend from heaven, with a shout, with the voice of the archangel, and with the trumpet of God: And the dead in Christ shall rise first."

5

Israel's Calendar Aligned with the Astronomical Calendar

The four previously mentioned individuals, Job, King Solomon, Deborah, and Gideon, are known to be in the correct locations and times of a known solar eclipse. They also use descriptive language describing the solar eclipses. With all data points lining up, one can easily conclude that they witnessed a solar eclipse. Since they witnessed such an event, one now has to ask whether the eclipses are enough to fulfill Scripture or demand that God perform a second miracle that cannot be explained. Since the first miracle of the solar eclipse occurrence is more than enough to explain the Scripture, the only reason to demand something else is self-desire.

God's preference for using solar eclipses to communicate with His chosen people is displayed in the four previously mentioned people. Since God used eclipses in the previously discussed interactions with His chosen people, it is reasonable to conclude that He used the same communication method for other individuals.

The timeframe from Abraham to Joshua would be the most amazing time to look for this communication from God. Abraham's description of a smoking oven with a torch and Joshua's commanding of the sun both appear to be solar eclipses. Historically Abraham's and Joshua's accounts have long been thought to be solar eclipses.

The difficulty with pinpointing the solar eclipses for Abraham and Joshua is finding the correct Exodus date. The Bible provides detailed sums of years between Abraham and Joshua. However, the Bible uses the Exodus as the primary focal point for the timeline. If the wrong year is assigned to the Exodus, then the wrong year will be assigned to Abraham and Joshua. The assigning of the wrong year to the Exodus has caused many to search for the eclipses in the wrong years. Assigning the correct year to the Exodus reveals the solar eclipses that line up with the accounts of Abraham and Joshua.

Historians traditionally take best guesses as to the correct placement of the Exodus. The timelines they create are bound primarily to themselves, not to a concrete timeline. Man's history can be manipulated, and if not paired with a concrete timeline, the resulting date could be off by a large sum of years.

On the other hand, the astronomical calendar is a consistent clockwork pattern that began at creation and will persist until termination. The timeline of the stars can be calculated with precision because no man has moved them.

Israel's calendar is based on the astronomical calendar. Ancient Israel started their months with the sighting of the new moon. The Bible has several recorded sabbaths and Passovers that happened after a precise length of time from the Exodus. Since Israel's sabbaths, Passovers, and days of weeks are provided in the Bible timeline and Israel's calendar is based on the astronomical calendar, one should be able to reconstruct the Israelites' calendar.

Reconstruction of Israel's calendar will allow us to align specific sabbaths mentioned in the Bible to Israel's calendar. Nowhere in the Bible would it be more amazing to align biblical sabbaths to Israel's lunar calendar than that around the Exodus, ultimately revealing the only acceptable Exodus date.[25] The Exodus date can be aligned with the astronomical timeline by considering Israel's lunar months with correlating Passovers and sabbaths.

The astronomical calendar events that can be used for locating the Exodus are the day when manna started to fall, the first Passover in the Promised Land, the day of the Exodus, and the Jubilee cycle. When all these events are put together, the star calendar's corresponding date would be the only correct calendar date for the Exodus.

A summary of the finding and the proposed Exodus year is based on chronological research located in appendices A, B, and C at the back of this book.

---

[25] Jeffrey Grimm, *Solar Eclipses in the Bible* (United States: Jeffrey Grimm 2021), appendices A and B.

The Exodus date of Saturday, April 17, 1524 BC, is the only date that allows Israel's astronomical calendar to occur as described. The following is a summary of the findings to demonstrate that the year 1524 BC fulfills all the biblical requirements of the Exodus.

1. The Passover occurred on a Friday, making the following morning the Exodus from Egypt on Saturday. The Passover Lambs were sacrificed on Friday, April 16, 1524. The Exodus from Egypt would then have occurred on Saturday, April 17, 1524 BC. The odds of this occurring as required is 1 in 7. When calculated with triangulation point number two the odds are 1 in 3

2. The Exodus date of 1524 BC allows for the appropriate timing of the manna. The promise of manna would have occurred on Saturday, 15 Ziv, after sunset. The manna would have fallen on the mornings of Sunday, 15 Ziv, Monday, 16 Ziv, Tuesday, 17 Ziv, Wednesday, 18 Ziv, Thursday, 19 Ziv, and Friday, 20 Ziv, but not on Saturday, 21 Ziv. The 1524 BC template shows that the events unfolded swiftly with no delay, matching the story from Josephus. God made the promise in the evening and sent the manna in the morning. The odds of this occurring as required are 2 in 7.

3. Precisely 40 years after the Exodus, Israel entered the Promised Land and had their Passover. With a 1524 BC Exodus, the first Passover in the Promised Land would have occurred on Friday to Saturday, April 23, 1484 BC. This would be in keeping with a conservative read

of the Mosaic Law regarding the Omer Offering. The odds of this occurring as required is 1 in 7.

4. The Exodus year of 1524 BC allows for the first jubilee to occur in 1477 BC, and the 18th jubilee would take place in the second year of King Zedekiah's reign. The odds of this occurring as required is 1 in 49.

An Exodus date of Saturday, April 17, 1524 BC, allows the jubilee and all three sabbaths to occur on the proper days of the timeline. The probability of all the triangulation datapoints lining up is $1/49 \times 1/7 \times 2/7 \times 1/3 = 1/3,601$, equaling 1 in 3,601. This means that 1 year in every 3,601 years will line up with the Exodus requirements. Considering that 1524 BC was about 3,544 years ago, there would only be one year from Moses to today that would fit all the requirements.

The Israelite lunar month study revealed that the only exodus date that facilitates all the Exodus requirements is Saturday, April 17, 1524 BC.

The last date calculated in appendix C of this book is the year God communicated with Abraham. For your convenience, an overview of the calculation is given here.

Subtracting 400 years from when Israel entered the Promised Land will give the year God and Abraham entered into a covenant. Subtract 400 years from 1484 BC gives us 1884 BC as the year God promised Abraham that his grandchildren would inherit the Promised Land in 400 years, the fourth generation.

71

6

Abraham's Oven and Torch

A few number of people in the Bible stand out who had pivotal moments impacting generations to come. Abraham entering the covenant with God is one of these moments. At that moment, the land of Canaan was established as the Promised Land for Israel. The covenant occurred at the exact location and time as a substantial solar eclipse. Abraham then compares his experience of the eclipse to an oven and torch. This chapter will look at the Bible's account for information that may help determine the event's timing.

Time

Appendices B and C introduce three important dates that are used in this chapter. First, 1884 BC will be used for the year God communicated with Abraham. Secondly, 1524 BC will be used for the exodus from Egypt. Lastly, April 23, 1484 BC, will be used for the first Passover held in the Promised Land.

Location

The exact location for the covenant ceremony between God and Abraham is elusive, although a general area is known. Abraham lived in the town called Hebron, located south of Jerusalem. Abraham left Hebron to save his nephew, and on his way back home, the king of Jerusalem met him in the Valley of Shaveh. The location of the Valley of Shaveh is not known but has been theorized to be around Jerusalem. The valley of Shaveh is the last location the Bible gives for Abraham before the event in question occurred.

To compound the problem, a timeframe between the events in the Valley of Shaveh to Abraham's vision is not given; there could be days or minutes between. The Bible just says, "After these things." Regardless, if one chooses to apply the location for the vision from God to the Valley of Shaveh or a different location. The safest option is that the vision from God occurred in the lower portion of Canaan between Jerusalem and Abraham's home on the southern border of the Promised Land.

Abraham's Knowledge

Understanding the event means understanding the knowledge that Abraham had concerning the stars. Josephus, who lived in the time of Jesus, would be acquainted with the Old Testament's theories and teachings that Jesus would have been accustomed to hearing. About the wisdom of Abraham, Josephus states, "Abraham communicated to them arithmetic, and delivered to them the science of astronomy; for, before Abram came into

Egypt, they were unacquainted with those parts of learning; for that science came from the Chaldeans into Egypt."[26]

Abraham was wise in the science of astronomy. Josephus tells us that the Chaldeans developed the science of astronomy. Abraham came from the city of Ur, which is the primary city of the Chaldeans. Abraham would have likely gained the knowledge of the city he lived in and that, in this case, would be the science of astronomy. Josephus then informs us that Abraham educated Egyptians on the science of astronomy.

Egyptians extensively documented their understanding of astronomy. For example, the Tomb of Senenmut has a star chart on the ceiling that documents the alignment of planets made in the 18th Dynasty of Egypt. This is the oldest star chart dating back to Moses' time and is an excellent example of the Egyptians' understanding of astronomy science.

Seeing that Abraham taught the Egyptians astronomy and understood astronomy's science, the following symbology during the event where God communed with him would not have escaped him.

Time of Eclipse and Bible History

Star charts indicate a rare phenomenon that occurred in the year 1884 BC. Star charts for 1884 BC indicate a total solar eclipse occurred in the area around where Abraham most likely was.

---

[26] Josephus, Translated by Whiston, *The Works of Flavius Josephus: Antiquities of the Jews* (London: John Bumpus, 1828), 1.8.2. p. 39.

The eclipse that occurred on the morning of September 15, 1884 BC, matches the event's scriptural description.

Abraham was 83 years old when God told him he would have a land inheritance for a son he did not have yet. The Lord communicated with Abraham starting at sunset on September 14 through the morning of September 15, 1884 BC. God then promised that, 400 years later, the land of Canaan would belong to his descendants. As promised, after 400 years and on the Passover of 1484 BC, the promise was fulfilled.[27]

The entire night of September 14, 1884 BC, and the subsequent eclipse on the morning of September 15, 1884 BC, meets all the descriptions laid down in Scripture as to the timing of the event when God spoke to Abraham.

The Stars

The event started when God appeared to Abraham in a vision:

Genesis 15:5 – "God brought Abraham forth abroad, and said, Look now toward heaven, and number the stars, if thou be able to number them: and he said unto him, So shall thy seed be."

Stars representing people is a reoccurring theme in the Bible. God told Abraham to count the stars that represented his descendants. Joseph represented people as stars:

---

[27] Jeffrey Grimm, *Solar Eclipses in the Bible: Finding Moses' Burning Bush* (United States: Jeffrey Grimm 2021), appendix C.

Genesis 37:9 – "Joseph dreamed yet another dream, and told it to his brethren, and said, Behold, I have dreamed yet a dream; and, behold, the sun and the moon and 11 stars made obeisance to me."

Josephus provides a commentary on this verse: "The moon and sun were like his mother and father; the former, as she that gave increase and nourishment to all things, and the latter, he that gave form and other powers to them; and that the stars were like his brethren, since they were eleven in number, as were the stars that receive their power from the sun and moon."[28]

People represented symbolically as stars occurred first with Abraham and such symbolism is embraced throughout the Bible. Jesus even identifies Himself as "the bright and morning star" (Revelation 22:16).

God reminds Abraham that He had been with him from the beginning: "God said unto him, I am Jehovah that brought thee out of Ur of the Chaldees, to give thee this land to inherit it" (Genesis 15:7). The vision brings up the fact that God brought Abraham out of the sinful city of Ur so that his children would inherit Canaan.

The Stage for the Covenant

God instructs Abraham to prepare the covenantal stage for the land promise: "Jehovah, whereby shall I know that I shall inherit it? And he said unto him, Take me a heifer of three years

---

[28] Josephus, Translated by Whiston, *The Works of Flavius Josephus: Antiquities of the Jews* (London: John Bumpus, 1828), 2.2.3, p. 54.

old, and a she-goat three years old, and a ram three years old, and a turtle-dove, and a young pigeon. And he took unto him all these, and divided them in the midst, and laid each half over against the other: but the birds divided he not" (Genesis 15:8-10). Thus, Abraham was commanded to cut one calf, one goat, and one ram in half.

Once the stage was prepared for the covenant, Abraham spent the rest of the day chasing away meat-eating birds: "And the birds of prey came down upon the carcasses, and Abram drove them away" (Genesis 15:11). Preparing three large animals for the covenant and chasing away the birds from the carcasses would have taken a substantial amount of energy, leaving Abraham exhausted by nightfall: "When the sun was going down, a deep sleep fell upon Abram; and, lo, a horror of great darkness fell upon him" (Genesis 15:12). Abraham chased birds away all day until the sun went down and darkness started covering the land.

One Night Two Events

Genesis 15:12 and Genesis 15:17 describe two different events. First, the sun prepares to go down and darkness covers the Earth in Genesis 15:12-16. The Bible states, "A deep sleep fell upon Abram; and, lo, a horror of great darkness fell upon him" (Genesis 15:12). The terminology "deep sleep" and "a horror of great darkness" would imply a longer span of time than the few minutes afforded at sunset. An entire night of darkness could be spoken of. The second event was "when the sun went down, and it was dark, behold, a smoking furnace, and a flaming torch that passed between these pieces." Genesis 15:17. This second event occurred any time after "a horror of great darkness" up to the sun's complete and uninterrupted rising in the morning.

Parallels can be seen when overlapping the Bible account and events from the night of September 14 through the morning of September 15, 1884 BC. Abraham is covered in darkness in what he considers to be some sort of sleeping vision. Abraham experienced "a horror of great darkness." This darkness of night lasted 11 hours. In the morning, the sunrise was a substantial eclipse that appeared to Abraham as a smoking oven and a flaming torch. Abraham would have known it was not a typical chain of events. This would have accurately described what Abraham saw if he witnessed this 11-hour night then the sunrise eclipse.

The First Event

The Bible informs us that "a deep sleep fell upon Abraham." Therefore, it is understandable that after a long day, Abraham would fall asleep at sunset; however, the following statement, "Lo, a horror of great darkness fell Upon him," describes a sense of awareness, so one is led to believe that Abraham has a vision at this moment. Whether the vision occurred in a night of sleep or with him awake, one can rest assured that God was with him and Abraham was aware of the event.

"A horror of great darkness fell upon him" describes the night in question on September 14, 1884 BC. Abraham's day started at sunset, and it started with a very dark night referred to as "great darkness." The night of September 14, 1884 BC, had no moon the entire night, making it very dark.

78

Combining bloody animal carcasses and the darkest night possible would have created a "horror" for Abraham. Lions, wolves, and bears lived in the area, and the risk of attack would make for a scary environment.

During the darkness, God communed with Abraham:

Genesis 15:13-16 – "God said unto Abram, know of a surety that thy seed shall be sojourners in a land that is not theirs, and shall serve them; and they shall afflict them four hundred years; and also that nation, whom they shall serve, will I judge: and afterward shall they come out with great substance. But thou shalt go to thy fathers in peace; thou shalt be buried in a good old age. And in the fourth generation they shall come hither again: for the iniquity of the Amorites is not yet full."

Abraham's descendants for four generations are equal to 400 years; they shall be sojourners. After 400 years, Abraham's children would come back to claim the Promised Land.

During the horror of great darkness, Abraham saw the stars that testified of God's desire. Recall that God had told him to "Look now toward heaven, and number the stars, if thou be able to number them: and he said unto him, So shall thy seed be" (Genesis 15:5). At the moment of God's communing with Abraham in complete darkness, he would have seen millions of stars. The millions of stars that Abraham counted had an assigned position among all the other stars (naturally, they would seem to move as the earth rotated). The stars that Abraham counted never move out of their assigned spot among all the constellations. The stars are so stationary relative to each other that the constellations that existed at the time of Abraham look the same today. Each star that Abraham counted represented a descendant of Abraham. He would have noticed that most of the stars did not move from their assigned locations; this symbolized that God was planning to give them a permanent home.

On the night of September 14, 1884 BC, through the morning of September 15, 1884 BC, Abraham counted four planets. At the moment of complete darkness, three planets, Venus, Jupiter, and Mars, would have been visible. By the end of the evening, Saturn would have come into view as well. A total of four planets were visible during the complete darkness that night. On this night, the moon and Mercury were not visible because they were close to the sun.

The four planets that Abraham counted each represent a generation. These four planets were known as wandering stars, because they behaved differently from all the other stars. Today, the wandering stars are called planets. The planets do not stay in one assigned location among the constellations. The planets change location continually without ceasing. On one day, Mars can be seen in the constellation Orion, and then on another night, Mars could be seen in Aquarius. All the planets have the same unique characteristics. This visual goes along exactly with what God had said. God told Abraham that his "seed shall be sojourners in a land that is not theirs" and then in "the fourth generation they shall come hither again." The visual of four stars sojourning continuously forever symbolized the four generations that would not know a permanent home.

The six wandering stars of Abraham's day were Mercury, Venus, Mars, Jupiter, Saturn, and the moon. Josephus tells us that Moses designed the candlestick that goes in the temple based on six planets and the sun: "the seven lamps signified the seven planets; for so many there were springing out of the candlestick."[29] The Israelites considered the sun as a planet. Josephus offered further explanation of this fact: "...spread itself into as many branches as there are planets, including the sun among them."[30] Amos expounds upon this to include heavenly forms: "Seek him that maketh the Pleiades and Orion, and turneth the shadow of death into the morning, and maketh the day dark with night" (Amos 5:8). God created the seven stars, constellations, and also total solar eclipses. Hence "maketh the day dark with night."

Abraham would have noticed four planets in the sky. At the beginning of the darkness, three planets were visible. At the end of the night, roughly one hour before sunrise, the last planet rose just over the constellation Virgo—symbolizing the sojourning of four generations.

A generation is subjective, but 400 years is a set amount of time. The four generations are a symbolic representation of 400 years. At the time of Abraham, a generation would be roughly 100 years. For instance, Abraham was 100 years old when he had his son Isaac, Jacob was 91 years old when he had Joseph, and Joseph died at 110 years old. The Bible states that

[29] Josephus, Translated by Whiston, *The Works of Flavius Josephus: Wars of the Jews (London: John Bumpus, 1828),* 5.5.5, p. 718.

[30] Josephus, Translated by Whiston, *The Works of Flavius Josephus: Antiquities of the Jews* (London: John Bumpus, 1828), 3.6.7, p. 89.

Abraham's children would be sojourners for 400 years, making these 400 years a definite timeframe. God then informs us that after four generations, Abraham's ancestors would return to the Promised Land. These timeframes must be equal, so by dividing 400 by four generations, we get 100 years for each generation. This may not mean there must be precisely one hundred years between each generation of parents and children or that each individual would live for precisely 100 years. Instead, a total period of roughly four generations a total of 400 years would pass.

God told Abraham, "Also that nation, whom they shall serve, will I judge: and afterward shall they come out with great substance" (Genesis 15:14). The moment God spoke these words, the night ended as the last planet started rising just above the constellation Virgo. The constellation Virgo marked the time of year that crops were harvested. Mid-September is when one's hard work is rewarded with a harvest that would bring wealth for their work, once again symbolizing that the fourth generation would receive wealth for their labor.

The Second Event

The night ended; however, the sun was about to go dark one last time. The rising of Virgo marked the end of the night that must have felt like a "horror of great darkness." The night lasted roughly 11 hours and must have felt like an eternity. The sun entered a noticeable eclipse at sunrise that climaxed in a 92% to 100% solar eclipse (depending on his location, which is unknown). The eclipse is recorded in the following verse, "It came to pass, that, when the sun went down, and it was dark,

82

behold, a smoking furnace, and a flaming torch that passed between those pieces" (Genesis 15:17).

The second event, the eclipse of the sun at sunrise, matches Scripture. There was an entire night of absolute darkness and then the sun went into an eclipse.

A deeper understanding of what Abraham saw can be gained by understanding what an "oven" is. Mr. Easton informs us that the Hebrew word for "oven" found in Genesis 15:17 is *tannur*. Easton describes the *tannur* as an "oven for baking bread. It was a large pot, narrowing towards the top."[31]

George A. Barton wrote about this oven in his book. He stated, "Each consist of a cylinder of baked earth about 2 feet in diameter and 1 1/2 inches thick. It is closed by a cover of the same material, in which a stone or lump of clay has been embedded as a handle. There is rarely any bottom except the bare earth. The loaves which were flat discs, were usually placed inside, either on the ground covered with clean pebbles or on a baking-tray." He goes on to state, "the fire was usually heaped about the outside of the oven."[32]

There are three critical things about the archeological descriptions of the oven. First, it is round in shape when standing over it, looking directly down on the oven. Second, the fire would be outside the oven, so any light from the fire will illuminate the outside, not the inside. Third, the oven center will

---

[31] M. G. Easton, *Illustrated Bible Dictionary (New York: Harper & Brothers, 1893), p. 269.*

[32] George A. Barton, *Archeology and the Bible*. (Philadelphia: American Sunday-School Union) p. 190.

be dark because the fire is outside the oven. A ring of smoke and fire can be seen as a result of the fire outside the oven.

The description of a smoking oven and torch matches the description of the solar eclipse. Ellicott believes that Abraham witnessed a total solar eclipse: "The terror was not mental so much as bodily, caused by a deep gloom settling round him, such as would be the effects of an eclipse of the setting sun, and shutting all mortal things away from his view."[33] Ellicott has Genesis 15:12 and 15:17 occurring at the same time. The Scripture does not provide any indication that the two recorded events are the same event. A literal reading of the Scripture would place the events of Genesis 15:12 and 15:17 in series, hence following each other—not cooccurring. With that said I agree with Ellicott's theory that Abraham is describing a solar eclipse in Genesis 15:17.

Over 4,000 years ago, people did not understand what caused a solar eclipse, let alone that they existed. The Hebrew language did not have a word for a total solar eclipse, making it impossible to relay what Abraham had seen in a meaningful language outside of symbolism. Abraham compared the total solar eclipse to something he and others of his time understood: a smoking oven and a torch.

---

[33] Payne Smith, Edited by John Ellicott, *A Bible Commentary for English Readers, Vol. I, Book of Genesis* (New York: Cassell, 1882) p. 67.

Abraham's Oven and Torch
Solar Eclipse September 15, 1884 BC.

Below is a side-by-side comparison of the account.
Left: is a solar eclipse with diamond ring effects.
Right: is a smoking furnace and flaming torch.

A side-by-side comparison of Abraham's experience and the total solar eclipse of September 15, 1884 BC, will show their similarities.

- **Abraham** – "When the sun was going down, a deep sleep fell upon Abram; and, lo, a horror of great darkness fell upon him" (Genesis 15:12).

- **Night of September 14, 1884 BC** – For 11 hours darkness covered Abraham, no light not even the moon.

- **Abraham** – "It came to pass, that, when the sun went down, and it was dark, behold, a smoking furnace, and a flaming torch that passed between those pieces" (Genesis 15:17).

- **Eclipse of September 15, 1884 BC** – The sun rose in the morning, but it went into a solar eclipse. At the time of a total solar eclipse, the moon is substantially in front of the sun, blocking the sunlight. The moon appears as a dark circle void of all light. A sliver of the sun could be seen that started at the lower left of the moon and then passed by way of the upper left side of the moon and exited on the upper right of the moon.

The side-by-side comparison of Abraham's experience and a total solar eclipse shows that Abraham's description is similar to the morning eclipse.

The Covenant

The interaction between God and Abraham was to form a covenant. The Bible states in Genesis 15:8-10 that God directed

Abraham to cut multiple animals in half and lay their halves opposite the other so that both parties can walk through the halves to confirm the covenant. Since God does not have a body to physically walk through the two pieces, God performed the act through the events described.

The darkness and the burning torch were God's presence moving between the two pieces, allowing God to ratify the covenant between Himself and Abraham. God appears in a solar eclipse represented by darkness and a smoking oven with a torch. In the event, Abraham believes that God moves through the animals' halves, confirming the covenant.

Matthew Poole's Commentary about this covenant states: "Both smoke and fire are elsewhere mentioned as the signs and means of God's appearance." He goes on to state, "because God hath no body which could visibly do so, therefore, he doth it in this type or shadow."[34]

Moses uses the same imagery of a smoking oven to represent God's presence among Israel on Mount Sinai:

Exodus 19:18 – "Mount Sinai, the whole of it, smoked, because Jehovah descended upon it in fire; and the smoke thereof ascended as the smoke of a furnace, and the whole mount quaked greatly."

Abraham believed that the image of a smoking oven in a dark sky was the very presence of God. Subsequently, the prophet

---

[34] Matthew Poole, Annotations upon the Holy Bible, Vol. I (London, 1700), p. 25.

Jeremiah confirms that God entered a covenant with Abraham and all of Israel:

Jeremiah 34:18 – "I will give the men that have transgressed my covenant, that have not performed the words of the covenant which they had made before me, when they cut the calf in twain and passed between the parts thereof."

Jeremiah is referencing this covenant between Abraham and God which extends to all of his descendants.

The solar eclipse described as an oven and torch was God's presence as He passed through the animals cut in half, ratifying the covenant with Abraham and his descendants.

Conclusion

Abraham witnessed a substantial solar eclipse and then exactly described that eclipse. Abraham was in the correct location and time to witness a substantial solar eclipse. Abraham then compares his experience of the eclipse to an oven and torch. Seeing that the eclipse fulfills all the biblical requirements, the only reason not to associate the eclipse with Abraham would be purely self-desire and not biblical necessity.

Symbology

By comparing the covenant ceremony with the fulfillment, a greater insight into the symbology can be gained.

The smoking oven that Abraham saw in the sky would represent Egypt. Just as a furnace separates impurities from gold, God used Egypt to purify Israel from their impurities. Egypt could be considered a furnace for Israel to the extent that Israel came into Egypt as "sojourners in a land that is not theirs" but exited with great possessions and numbers that would enable them to claim the Promised Land. The fire coming out of the oven would represent God leading Israel out of Egypt to be his people.

Moses, in Deuteronomy 4:20, along with the writers of 1 Kings 8:51 and Jeremiah 11:4, confirm that Egypt would be the iron furnace and God delivered them to be his people.

Deuteronomy 4:20 – "But Jehovah hath taken you, and brought you forth out of the iron furnace, out of Egypt, to be unto him a people of inheritance, as at this day."

1 Kings 8:51 – "For they are thy people, and thine inheritance, which thou broughtest us forth out of Egypt, from the midst of the furnace of iron."

Jeremiah 11:4 – "Which I commanded your fathers in the day that I brought them forth out of the land of Egypt, out of the iron furnace, saying, Obey my voice, and do them, according to all which I command you: so shall ye be my people, and I will be your God."

The image of a furnace is symbolically tied to God:

Psalm 12:6 – "The words of Jehovah are pure words; as silver tried in a furnace on the earth, purified seven times."

Ezekiel 22:17-19 – "And the word of Jehovah came unto me, saying, Son of man, the house of Israel has become dross unto me: all of them are brass and tin and iron and lead, in the midst of the furnace; they are the dross of silver. Therefore thus saith the Lord Jehovah: Because ye are all become dross, therefore, behold, I will gather you into the midst of Jerusalem."

Matthew 13:50 – "And shall cast them into the furnace of fire: there shall be the weeping and gnashing of teeth."

Malachi 4:1 – "For, behold, the day cometh, it burneth as a furnace; and all the proud, and all that work wickedness, shall be stubble; and the day that cometh shall burn them up, saith Jehovah of hosts, that it shall leave them neither root nor branch."

God's Presence Is Like a Furnace:

Zechariah 13:9 – "And I will bring the third part into the fire, and will refine them as silver is refined, and will try them as gold is tried. They shall call on my name, and I will hear them: I will say, It is my people; and they shall say, Jehovah is my God."

Isaiah 1:25 – "I will turn my hand upon thee, and thoroughly purge away thy dross, and will take away all thy tin."

7

Joshua's Sun Stopped

The battle of Gibeon was won due to Joshua commanding the moon and sun to obey him. This miraculous event has long been thought to be a solar eclipse. However, the exact solar eclipse has proved elusive. The exact eclipse will be located using the date for God's and Abraham's covenant solar eclipse and the Exodus date established in appendices B and C. With the perspective of the correct eclipse, the day's events will be fully revealed as never before.

Joshua's eclipse will strengthen the established timeline for the exodus of Israel. The Bible informs us that 400 years lapsed from the covenant with Abraham to the possession of the Promised Land. Within seven years of entering the Promised Land, Joshua's eclipse occurred. Identifying the eclipse at the location and time that the Bible describes will strengthen the established timeline.

Location

The location where Joshua commanded the sun and moon was in Gibeon. The city of Gibeon was located on the top of a mountain about 6 miles northwest of Jerusalem and 15 miles west of Gilgal.

A truce was made between Gibeon and Israel, but three days later, Israel discovered the four cities of Gibeon (Gibeon, Chephirah, Beeroth, and Kirjath Jearim) were only between fifteen and twenty miles away instead of the assumed many, many miles away from the Promised Land.

Timing

The Battle for Gibeon occurred between 40 and 47 years after the Exodus from Egypt. Israel exited Egypt on Saturday morning, April 17, 1524 BC.[35] During the summer of 1522 BC, Israel sent Caleb to spy on Canaan. Caleb was 40 years old at the time. After 40 years in the wilderness, Israel celebrated their first Passover in the Promised Land on the sabbath day April 23, 1484 BC. On the Day of Atonement, September 24, 1477 BC, the year Caleb turned 85, all the land was divided, and Israel celebrated their first Jubilee.

The timing of the events mentioned within Joshua chapter 10 must have happened between the first Passover in the Promised Land on April 23, 1484 BC, and the first Jubilee held on September 24, 1477 BC. The book of Joshua provides a detailed

---

[35] Jeffrey Grimm, *Solar Eclipses in the Bible* (United States: Jeffrey Grimm 2021), appendices A and B.

chronology of events but with no recorded length of time between events. We know the earliest date the event could have occurred is after the arrival into the Promised Land being 40 years after the exodus from Egypt on April 17, 1524 BC. The end date is calculated based on Caleb's age. Caleb was 40 years old when he spied out the land of Canaan just over two years after leaving Egypt. Joshua then tells us Caleb was 85 years old when the land of Canaan was divided. The Bible is silent about any further dates, just that it is based on Caleb's age and chronology of events.

Some authors have used this space of no dates to impose their own theories. One popular theory used by Ussher places a seven-year sabbatical six months after crossing the Jordan. According to Archbishop Ussher, Israel walked into the Promised Land of Canaan and completed all their conquests from April to August. Ussher only provides six months for every battle to occur. Ussher apparently was trying to line up post-Babylonian captivity reports of sabbatical years. He declared a seven-year sabbatical *before* the land was divided— doing nothing: "And thus ended that most busy year of the world, 2553. In the first six months, where of Moses conquered all that land over the Jordan, toward the east, and in the later, Joshua conquered the most part of all, that lay to the west of it: and in the midst of the year, manna ceasing, the people of Israel began to live upon the food in the land of Canaan."[36]

Archbishop Ussher determines that the entire battle sequence from Passover up to but not including the last battle only took six months. There is no internal documentation within the book

---

[36] James Ussher, *The Annals of the World* (London: Tyler, 1658), p. 28.

of Joshua that collaborates with this. The Bible does not state how much time passed between every single battle. There could have been one year between every single battle spoken of in Joshua, or they could have been fought back-to-back, or there could have been a seven-year space between any other battle; the timing is not known, because the Bible is silent on this.

The only timeframes given in the book of Joshua are that 40 years after exiting Egypt, Israel crossed the Jordan river then seven years later the land was divided. The seven-year window was April 1484 BC when Israel entered the Promised Land up to the Day of Atonement on 1477 BC when Caleb was 85 years old. The seven-year span is the only time identified within Joshua; therefore, the battle at Gibeon must have taken place within this seven-year window.

One event in this timeframe that stands out is a solar eclipse on June 1, 1478 BC. The solar eclipse occurred inside the window established with the Passover on 1484 BC to the Jubilee of 1477 BC. This date for the last big battle in the conquest of Canaan makes more sense being one year from the dividing up of the land versus the seven years proposed by Ussher.

Story of Gibeon

Joshua 10:6-9 – "And the men of Gibeon sent unto Joshua to the camp to Gilgal, saying, Slack not thy hand from thy servants; come up to us quickly, and save us, and help us: for all the kings of the Amorites that dwell in the hill country are gathered together against us. So Joshua went up from Gilgal, he, and all the people of

95

war with him, and all the mighty men of valor. And Jehovah said unto Joshua, fear them not: for I have delivered them into thy hands; there shall not a man of them stand before thee. Joshua therefore came upon them suddenly, for he went up from Gilgal all night."

The walk to Gibeon was an arduous, moonless, all-night march of about 15 miles as the crow flies over rugged terrain. The troops would not be able to run, for they would trip. The darkness lasted for about 10 hours that night, so it is reasonable to estimate that Israel arrived at Gibeon shortly after sunrise. Gilgal sits at roughly 1,000 feet below sea-level while Gibeon sits at 2,500 feet above sea-level, so the walk would have been chiefly uphill as they weaved up and down the mountain range. Israel walked all night for about 12 hours and over 15 miles, arriving about the time of the noticeable eclipse. Israel's arrival at Gibeon and the solar eclipse surprised the Canaanites, causing them to flee. The Israelites pursued them to Azekah and Makkedah. God caused a hailstorm to crush the Canaanite army as they ran away. More Canaanites died from the hailstorm than from Israel. Joshua commanded the sun on this day, resulting in the sun not setting for about a full day (Joshua 10:12-14).

Solar Eclipse

The skies above Gibeon experienced a rare astronomical event within the set timeframe.

On May 31, 1478 BC, the day of the Jewish calendar was 29 Sivan. The moon would not rise until the next night, so the night of the march was a very dark, moonless night. The daytime hours were from 5:00 AM to 7:00 PM, giving 14 hours of sunlight, making it one of the year's longest days.

The eclipse started around 6:30 AM. The sun went into a noticeable eclipse covering about 60% of the sun's surface at around 6:55 AM, two hours after sunrise. A maximum eclipse of 92% of the sun's surface occurred around 7:10 AM.

Three Retellings of War at Gibeon

Joshua 10:10-14 consists of 3 different retellings of the battle at Gibeon that started at sunrise and ended at sunset. Each retailing covers events that occurred at the beginning, middle, and end of the battles. While the retellings follow each other in the Bible, they more accurately happened simultaneously. The three retellings have the same starting point, being Gibeon, the start of the battle, and the same endpoint as the end of the battle.

Some people want to place Joshua 10:12-14 to follow those in Joshua 10:10 and 10:11 chronologically. However, doing so produces a contradiction. Joshua 10:10 tells us that "Jehovah discomfited them before Israel, and he slew them with a great slaughter at Gibeon, and chased them by way of the ascent of Beth-horon, and smote them to Azekah, and unto Makkedah." The battle started in Gibeon and ended in Azekah and Makkedah, so the fight is over if this is in absolute order. However, Joshua 10:11 places us back at the descent to Beth-horon with a subsequent pursuit to Azekah again.

Therefore, Joshua 10:11 must be retelling the battle unless we believe the battle was fought again in the same order of locations. Joshua 10:10-11, with its two retellings of the entire battle from start to finish, leaves no more room for further battles since they both cover the exact start-to-end locations. However, Joshua 10:12-13 retells the entire battle again as it states, "Then spoke Joshua to Jehovah in the day when Jehovah delivered up the Amorites before the children of Israel; and he said in the sight of Israel, Sun, stand thou still upon Gibeon; And thou, moon, in the valley of Aijalon. And the sun stood still, and the moon stayed, until the nation had avenged themselves of their enemies. Is not this written in the book of Jashar? And the sun stayed in the midst of heaven, and hasted not to go down about a whole day." The sun was commanded to stand still at Gibeon where the battle began and did not sit for about a day "until the nation had avenged themselves of their enemies." If the entire battle was first fought in Joshua 10:10 and then completely refought in Joshua 10:11, why do we find Israel given a whole additional day to avenge themselves again in Joshua 10:12-14?

If the battle is won, why would Joshua command the sun to stay up for a whole day until the battle was over—especially if the battle was already over? The answer is that these are three retellings of the same battle. A clearer image of this can be seen by organizing the events in chronological order. Let us cluster all the like parts out of these three retellings to make one whole story in proper occurrence.

The first timeline cluster depicts God's routing of the Canaanite army, forcing them to run because of the eclipsing sun. "Jehovah discomfited them before Israel" (Joshua 10:10). "As they fled from before Israel" (Joshua 10:11) and "sun, stand thou still upon Gibeon" (Joshua 10:12-13).

The second timeline cluster depicts the hail striking and killing the enemy army as they ran down the hill from Gibeon to Beth-horon: "Jehovah slew them with a great slaughter at Gibeon" (Joshua 10:10). "While they were at the descent of Bethhoron, that Jehovah cast down great stones from heaven upon them unto Azekah, and they died" (Joshua 10:11).

The third timeline cluster depicts Israel's pursuit of the enemy, killing them all the way to Makkedah: "Chased them by the way of the ascent of Beth-horon, and smote them to Azekah, and unto Makkedah" (Joshua 10:10). "More who died with hailstones than they whom the children of Israel slew with the sword" (Joshua 10:11). "And the sun stood still and the moon stayed, until the nation had avenged themselves of their enemies…and the sun stayed in the midst of the heaven, and hasten not to go down about a whole day" (Joshua 10:13).

Placing all three retellings on one timeline allows for a more straightforward observation of the day's events.

Before looking at the overarching timeline, it is essential to understand the third event. Joshua 10:12-14 is the supernatural event that makes this entire battle a miracle. Let us take a minute to look at this third retelling in more detail.

Joshua 10:12-14 informs us of the events in the heavens as the day unfolded. Joshua 10:13 tells us that the sun and the moon were in the sky. The exact locations are told as the sun stands still over Gibeon, and the moon stays in the Valley of Aijalon.

The translated word for the Hebrew word *dom* found in Joshua 10:13 is debated among scholars. The Hebrew word used to describe the action of the sun is *dom*. A popular way to translate *dom* in this verse is "stand still." Two popular Bible commentators, Clarke and Dr. Wilson, interpret *dom* to mean something different.

Adam Clarke believes *dom* means "silent" or "inactive." Clarke also believes the Hebrew word *amad* in reference to the moon means "stood still." He goes on to state, "Both moon and the sun were kept above the horizon, probably for the space of a whole day."[37] Adam Clarke believes that the moon and the sun sat in the same spot for an extra-long day. Adam Clarke concludes that God no longer caused the earth to spin on its axis. In order to achieve this, the earth would have to stop spinning entirely or substantially slow down. This conclusion could be reached from this poetic statement in Joshua 10. However, the consequences of an Earth slowing down or stopping and then rapidly accelerating again would be detrimental to all the earth's inhabitants.

God created everything, and He can do anything He wants, including stop the earth's rotation. The earth rotates on its axis to produce the day and night as it orbits the sun. The slowing down or stopping of the earth's rotation would be required to make the day longer. The earth spins at a speed of roughly 1,000 miles an hour. Immediately stopping the earth's rotation would likely rip apart entire mountain ranges, let alone what would happen to everything else. Everything on the planet would die. Again, God is capable of doing anything He wants. God could have slowed down or stopped the rotation of the earth, but if He

---

[37] Adam Clarke, *The Holy Bible: A Commentary and Critical Notes, Vol. II, Joshua to Esther* (New York: Lane & Sandford, 1842), p. 47.

did, God would have had to perform many more miracles to preserve the life of everything on earth.

This raises the question: Did God perform many miracles that day or did He perform one through natural phenomenon? A God that knows the future can build events into the creation of the world. Since God knew the future before the beginning of time, He could build miracles into the creation. For example, God could have created the clockwork of the solar system to incorporate this eclipse to save His people. This stance would require that God knew precisely when His people would be at that exact location before time began.

Suppose God planned for the eclipse to occur that day at that minute in that location, then no other work would be needed. One way that God could have provided for this exact moment without augmenting His own physical laws would be to build an eclipse into creation. Creating this event would become an Ebenezer, an object that would mark God's people's most pivotal moment.

Before the event, "Joshua said in the sight of Israel, Sun, stand thou still upon Gibeon; and thou, Moon, in the valley of Aijalon." This raises the question if God planned for this solar eclipse at the time He made the heavens, did Joshua's request have any bearing on the eclipse? If one confines God to our reality that time is sequential and therefore impossible to know the future, then no it did not. On the other hand if one views God as all-knowing and able to know everything past, present, and future, then yes. This book views God as all-knowing and therefore able to build Joshua's request into the astronomical timeline.

Professor Dr. Robert Wilson believes the Hebrew word *dom* used in Joshua 10:13 means "to be dark," and is equivalent to "eclipse." Professor Dr. Robert Wilson, in the article, "What Does the Sun Stood Still Mean?", stated:

"The region of Joshua's battle. It seems quite probable therefore from a scientific standpoint that there may have been an eclipse in this same region several centuries earlier, which would satisfy all the conditions. Could this be established, it would throw most welcome life upon the chronology of this early period. It is very desirable that this question should be fully investigated; but in the present strenuous times the writer has not time for the heavy computations involved."[38]

The solar eclipse that Professor Dr. Robert Wilson determined to have occurred is the total solar eclipse of June 1, 1478 BC.

A total solar eclipse passed on the opposite side of the Jordan and was 90% eclipsed over Gibeon. There must have been clouds in the sky, seeing that heavy hail fell on Israel's enemies shortly after Israel arrived at Gibeon. As the eclipse started, a dark circle blocked out the sun, visible through the clouds. By a maximum eclipse of over 90%, a crescent would have appeared in the sky. Observers may have realized this was the moon blocking the sun. At 90% eclipsed, most of the light would have been removed from the earth. With heavy cloud coverage, it would have been even darker. At the sight of the

---

[38] Dr. Robert Wilson, *"What Does the Sun Stood Still Mean?"* (Moody Monthly, October 1920).

sky getting dark, Israel's enemies could have become very frightened.

The day started with the eclipse over Gibeon, and after a long day of battle, when Israel was walking back, they would have been around Beth-Horon looking westward over the Valley of Aijalon. The moon would have come into view shortly after sunset at 6:50 PM. With the correct viewing angle such as proposed over the Valley of Aijalon, Israel would have had an unobstructed view of the moon at sunset, biblically referred to as the new moon.

The sequence of events that allows both these events to occur on the same day requires a solar eclipse in the morning. In this case, the solar eclipse occurred in the early morning, with the maximum eclipse occurring around 7:15 AM. June 1, 1478 BC, was one of the longest days of the year, so the sun did not set until 6:50 PM from the eclipse to sunset was 11 and a half hours. In this time, the moon has moved 1/60 of its way around the earth and 6 degrees away from the sun. These 11 hours and 30 minutes allow the moon to be visible after sunset for 20 minutes.

The moon rose at the end of the day over the valley of Aijalon. The moon becoming visible after sunset is possible, since the moon was 11.5 hours old. The sighting of the new moon triggered the blowing of the ram's horns. Thus, Israel celebrated the start of their new month and the victory handed to them by God. All this occurred at the setting sun after a long day of war.

Weather

> **Joshua 10:11** – And it came to pass, as they fled from before Israel, while they were at the descent of Beth-horon, that Jehovah cast down great stones from heaven upon them unto Azekah, and they died: they were more who died with hailstones than they whom the children of Israel slew with the sword.

The path that the kings ran in was downhill. The kings started at Gibeon, an altitude of 2,500 feet. They then ran to the Valley of Aijalon that sets at 1,000 feet above sea level. When the army of Canaan saw the extreme solar eclipse, they began to flee, running downhill away from Gibeon and the army of Israel. Seeing that they are running down the mountain, there would be a distance between them and Israel's army.

The LORD cast down great hailstones from heaven on the enemies of Israel. The term "cast down" would refer to the originating from a high place and then falling to the ground. Hailstones originate in the heavens and fall to the ground, so implying hailstones to be what fell would appear appropriate. Moving through the pass down the mountainside would have left them exposed to the weather with minimal options to escape the hail. At this point, a hailstorm dropping hail large enough to kill people descended on them and killed them. This is also one reason why Israel's army did not get harmed by the hail, because there was a distance between them.

The effects of an eclipse on the weather have not been studied in depth. What is known is temperatures can drop upwards of 10 degrees. The drop in temp creates a wind in the areas experiencing roughly 90% of an eclipse and then dies down in the area experiencing 100% of an eclipse. The lack of knowledge about the impact eclipses have on the weather is echoed by NOAA. Just before the total solar eclipse of 2017, NOAA stated:

> "Meteorologists and weather modelers will have different questions, like how will the eclipse affect temperature, or the speed and direction of low-level winds? Will the loss of sunlight affect weather events in progress, such as thunderstorms?"[39]

The answer follows:

> "On Monday, 21 August, 2017, during the solar eclipse, severe thunderstorms impacted the region producing: large hail, damaging winds, and locally heavy rain. Scattered thunderstorms began to develop early in the morning across central South Dakota, then became strong to severe as it approached the Missouri River Valley by mid to late morning. The biggest hail size of 2 inches (egg size) was reported at Olivet, SD, in Hutchinson County."[40]

[39] "NOAA Scientists Get Rare Chance to Study the Effects of an Eclipse on Weather." n.d. Welcome to NOAA Research. Accessed April 20,2021. https://research.noaa.gov/article/ArtMID/587/ArticlelD/57/NOAA-scientists-get-rare-chance-to-study-the-effects-of-an-eclipse-on-weather.

[40] US Department of Commerce, NOAA. n.d. "Solar Eclipse Day Storm Summary – August 21 2017." www.weather.gov. Accessed April 20, 2021. https://www.weather.gove/fsd/20170821-severestorms-solareclipse.

The total solar eclipse moved over the region of South Dakota around 10 o'clock. The timing appears to have amplified the weather, particularly in the formation of large hailstones. The appearance of these large hailstones correlates to just after the time of the total solar eclipse.

During the eclipse of 2017 AD, a small section of the central United States experienced a storm system moving through the area. When the eclipse went over the storm system, the rapid cooling and rewarming of the area turned it into a severe storm. The total solar eclipse appears to have amplified the instability of the weather system, producing large hailstones.

Hailstorms can occur any time of the year but are more common in spring and early summer. For hail to form, a specific weather condition needs to exist. First, moisture needs to be present in the air. Second, the air at the ground level must be hot enough to push straight up into the upper atmosphere, taking the moisture with it. Lastly, the upper atmosphere needs to be cool enough to freeze the moisture carried up into it. The stronger the updraft of current and the more moisture in this draft of current, the larger the hail becomes. Spring and early summer usually offer the prime condition for this phenomenon to occur. There are hot temperatures in the lower atmosphere in late summer and fall, but the upper atmosphere is too warm to freeze the moisture. Winter has a cold upper atmosphere, but the lower atmosphere is also cold. The general rule of thumb for hail is spring to early summer. With that said, weather conditions can change and produce any weather, any time of year.

Another interesting point is that the eclipse that covered Joshua occurred on June 1, 1478 BC. This eclipse's timing would place it in the prime time for a hailstorm seeing that there would be moisture in the air coming out of springtime, the ground layer would be warm, and the upper atmosphere would be cold. This could have been the catalyst to create super hail, something large enough to wipe out the entire army.

Joshua's Story from the Perspective of an Eclipse

This section is a hypothetical story based on the above facts.

The sunset on May 31, 1478 BC, was 29 Sivan of the Jewish calendar. The new month was to begin with the sighting of the new moon at sunset within the next two days. On this day, 29 Sivan, the message came to Joshua that Gibeon was under siege. Joshua gathered the army and set out, marching through the dark, moonless night. With no moon in the sky, the walk would be challenging. In addition to no light, the terrain they crossed was some of the most mountainous in the region. There is more than half a mile altitude shift between the starting location to the destination, indicating that they were walking uphill, for the most part, all night. At roughly two hours after sunrise, 7:00 AM in the morning, Israel arrived at Gibeon.

The sky would have been covered with clouds seeing that a hailstorm fell shortly after their arrival. The sun could be visible through some of the thinner clouds in the sky, allowing for observation of the sun.[41]

---

[41] **Warning**: *looking at the sun without appropriate safety equipment is dangerous and can result in permanent eye damage causing loss of sight.*

Before Israel's confrontation between the armies of Canaan at Gibeon, Joshua requested God to stop the sun over Gibeon and the moon in the Valley of Aijalon. As a result of Joshua's request, Israel expected the sun to go out over Gibeon and they expected to see the new moon after sunset that evening in the Valley of Aijalon.

Everyone at Gibeon would have noticed the sun through the clouds as a dark circular object moved in front of it. At the point of maximum eclipse, almost all the sun was blocked out by the circular object. Over 90% of the light was removed from the sky. The thick cloud coverage amplified the darkness to the point of complete darkness.

Israel was expecting this darkness to occur shortly after sunrise. Joshua spoke to God requesting the sun to stop. When the sun eventually stopped, Israel knew God had blessed their mission. The fulfillment of God stopping the sun caused Israel to rally.

The army of Canaan did not expect this eclipse, and it terrified them. The Canaanite army expected the sun to come up as usual, but when it went dark, it produced pure terror. Moreover, the terror was amplified by the sight of Israel rallying at the event—as if it had been expected.

The sight of an eclipsing sun and the arrival of the Israeli army would have the potential to "discomfit" the enemy of Israel.

R. Meir said: When the sun and the moon are eclipsed, it is a bad sign to the enemies of the Israelites (meaning, the Israelites themselves), because they are used to troubles: it is equal to the teacher's coming to the school with his whip in his hand. Who is more afraid? The child used to being beaten. This is the case when Israel does not do the will of the Creator; but when they do, they need not fear anything, as it is written Jeremiah, x. 82: "Thus hath said the Lord: Do not habituate yourselves in the way of the nations, and at the signs of the heavens be ye not dismayed; although the nations should be dismayed at them."[42]

The statement by R. Meir is an accurate description of what occurred during Joshua's conquest of Canaan. Meir points out that when a total solar eclipse occurs, it is terrible news to the world, but not to Israel because Israel is used to trouble and their adversaries are not. This applies to Israel and the kings of Canaan. Israel just came out of captivity in Egypt, where they saw unmentionable hurdles and oppression. They then wandered in the wilderness, facing major hurdles every step of the way. Through all these trials, Israel was victorious because God was taking care of them. Israel was used to rough times, but they learned to trust that everything would work out. On the other hand, the kings of Canaan lived in relative peace, not knowing troubles. While a solar eclipse occurred over both Israel and Canaan, Israel took the fear and channeled it into trust in God, while the kings of Canaan did not have this ability and rather feared the moment.

The Canaanite army, in their pure moment of terror ran as fast as they could. The egress for the enemy army was directly downhill toward the town of Beth-horon. The pass was steep,

---

[42] Translated by Michael L. Rodkinson, New Edition of The Babylonian Talmud, vol VII, "Festivals" (Boston: New Talmud Publishing Company, 1899), p. 40.

so they moved fast, putting distance between themselves and Israel. This pass left them exposed on the side of the mountain. In their exposure, God sent a hailstorm that was amplified into a severe hailstorm due to the solar eclipse. The severe hailstorm crushed and killed most of the Canaanite army. As told, more people died to hail than from the sword.

That evening, at sunset, while standing on a mountain pass where a hailstorm wiped out the majority of the Canaanite army, looking directly west at the setting sun over the Valley of Aijalon, the new moon would have been visible for 20 minutes, marking the new month. The ram's horns announced the beginning of the new month and the celebration of God's deliverance from their enemies.

Conclusion

The recorded environmental events about the battle of Gibeon are similar to that which would be reported if viewing the solar eclipse of 1478 BC. If the solar eclipse fulfills all scriptural requirements of the witnessed sun and moon actions, not associating the two would be born out of personal preference versus fact-based conclusions.

8

Moses' Burning Bush

The three parties of the Exodus believed a god was responsible for the events that occurred. However, the three parties could not agree on which god was responsible. After the Egyptians witnessed the birth of Horus, the first-born son of Osiris, at the same time of Isis' birth, they believed their god Horus was coming to save them. After Israel saw the total solar eclipse within the bull's horns and the Exodus from Egypt, Israel believed the Apis bull god had saved them. After Moses experienced the total solar eclipse in the form of a burning bush, Moses believed the Exodus was because of Israel's God.

The exploration of the astronomical events will solve one of the biggest questions in the Bible being: how one chain of events could have three such different responses.

Location

There are two locations of interest for this chapter. The first location is Egypt where Israel lived and Pharaoh resisted

Moses. The tribe of Israel lived in Goshen, lower Egypt, and left from Pi-Rameses, also known as Avaris. Pharaoh most likely lived in the capital of Egypt called Thebes.

The second location is Mount Sinai where God communicated with Moses in the mountains outside of Egypt. The exact location of the burning bush is not known. What is known is that Israel left Egypt and went to the Mountain of the Lord. This mountain is the same mountain where Moses saw the burning bush and where God told Moses to bring Israel. Most Bible scholars believe the Mountain of the Lord where Moses witnessed the burning bush is located somewhere in the Sinai Peninsula. However, the exact location is not known. Many locations have been proposed, but no agreement on one mountain has been reached.

Two Events

This chapter will look at two events and how they affected three different groups of people. The first event is a total solar eclipse over Egypt and the Sinai Peninsula. The second event is the Exodus from Egypt with a rare astronomical event in the sky around this time.

Timing

The last plague on Egypt is prophesied in Exodus 11:1-8, and the timing of this last plague is established in Exodus 12:2, which says, "This month shall be unto you the beginning of months; it shall be the first month of the year to you." Ancient Israel started the first day of the month with the sighting of the first crescent moon at sunset on April 2, 1524 BC. Therefore, the Israelite's Exodus would have occurred on 15 Nisan, April 17, 1524 BC. Conversely, the Egyptian's first day of the year started with the last sighting of the moon before being visually obstructed by the sun on March 31, 1524 BC. By examining the events of the days spanning from March 31, 1524 BC, through April 17, 1524 BC, details from the last of the ten plagues upon Egypt will emerge that have been lost to time.

Total Solar Eclipse

The timing of the solar eclipse coincides with Moses seeing the burning bush. Moses saw the burning bush before the Exodus in 1524 BC. One event that meets all the requirements of this event is the total solar eclipse of 1533 BC.

On May 9, 1533 BC, the sun was located in the constellation of Taurus the bull and, more specifically, between the horns. About 30 minutes before sunset, the sun went into a total solar eclipse for up to three minutes, totality occurring at 6:00 PM. The sunset occurred at about 6:30 PM, while the sun was 50% eclipsed. Israel, while slaves in Egypt and Moses at Mount Sinai, were in the optimal locations and times to witness this ring of fire.

The total solar eclipse impacted all the Sinai Peninsula and surrounding areas. On May 9, 1533 BC, a total solar eclipse passed over lower Egypt and most of the Sinai Peninsula. The 100% totality path was about 150 miles wide and centered directly over Thebes, Egypt, and then proceeded through the Sinai Peninsula.

**Taurus / Burning Bush
Total Solar Eclipse May 9, 1533 BC.**

Total solar eclipse between horns of
Taurus the bull constellation.

The entire Sinai Peninsula experienced a 100% totality except for the extreme north and south. Egypt experienced totality at Avaris/Pi-Ramesses, Giza, Thebes, Memphis, and Heliopolis. The eclipse's totality then moved over the Sinai Peninsula, covering most of the proposed sites for Mount Sinai.

Noteworthy locations that experienced totality in the Sinai Peninsula are Saint Catherine's Monastery, Mount Serbal, Mt. Sin Bisher, Mt. Khashm, Mount Seir, Mt. Paran, Hashem el-Tarif, and Gebel Khashm et-Tarif. The eclipse ended in Arabia with a 100% eclipse at sunset with the potential for a 100% eclipse at Mount Jabal Al Lawz and Mount Jebel Musa. In addition to the 100% eclipsed locations, Mount Karkom was at 99.9% and Petra at 99.4%.

The areas that experienced the 99.4% and 99.9% solar eclipse would still allow for the viewing of the sun's corona in addition to the phenomenon known as Bailey's beads or the diamond ring effect. Everywhere in the Sinai Peninsula and the immediate surrounding area has a burning ring of fire in the sky at sunset. All mentioned sites, and many others, provided the view of a substantial solar eclipse that would have overtaken the sun and left a burning ring of fire.

Egypt at the Time of the Exodus

The Egyptians viewed the astronomical events surrounding the Exodus differently than the Israelites. The Egyptians' culture and religion led them to believe that their gods would protect them, even though God was against the Egyptians—hence God's statement of hardening Pharaoh's heart. To understand the Egyptians' point of view and how God hardened their hearts, it is essential to take a brief survey of their false gods.

The Egyptians worshiped many gods believed to live all around them. The three primary gods were Osiris, Seth, and Isis. The three gods were brothers and sisters. Seth ruled over the desert and was known for being one that brought opposition. Osiris ruled over the Egyptians in the towns and was known as the chief god that brought peace. Isis was known for her ability to heal people. Osiris and Isis got married which made Seth jealous. Seth killed Osiris and chopped him into many pieces, which were hidden throughout Egypt. With Osiris dead, Seth became the prime ruler of the world. Seth's rule over the world brought opposition, not peace. Isis searched the land and found all the pieces of Osiris, putting Osiris back together. Once Osiris was put back together, Isis brought him back to life. However, Osiris no longer could rule over the living, only of the dead.

Osiris and Isis had a baby they called Horus. Horus was able to rule over the living, so he challenged his uncle Seth for rulership over the people. Horus won the battle and brought peace back to the land.

Isis continued her pursuit to bring life to Osiris, driving her to take a barren cow that cannot have babies and make it pregnant. The calf became the vessel that Osiris used to live on earth among his people. This calf grew into a bull known as the Apis Bull and is considered to be Osiris living among the Egyptians. When the Apis Bull died, it was buried as royalty and a new Apis Bull was found.

This quick breakdown of Egyptian mythology is not meant to be an exhaustive review but shows the primary figures that played a big part in the Egyptian culture at the Exodus time.

In addition to the Egyptian gods' mythology, it is essential to look at how the Egyptian gods are thought to interact with the Egyptians. The Egyptian gods are said to live in the night sky. The constellations were associated with their gods, the primary one being the constellation Taurus, the bull, associated with the Apis Bull god. The moon was associated with the goddess Isis, and the planet Jupiter was said to be Osiris or Horus, depending on if it was a morning or evening star.

Taurus, the bull, is associated with the chief deity of Egypt called Osiris. Osiris is also represented by the planet Jupiter when an evening star. When Jupiter becomes a morning star, Osiris is resurrected to living as his son Horus. In addition to the star's movement, Osiris is linked to the Apis bull. Osiris is the husband of the goddess Isis, who is also Osiris' sister. The Apis Bull is considered to be Isis' son. Therefore, the cow that gave birth to the Apis Bull is called the Isis Cow. The Apis Bull is then considered to have the spirit of Osiris in it.

The Apis Bull was arguably one of the most important gods of the Egyptian culture. The Apis bull was considered the life of Osiris and upon death would become one with Osiris in the heavens. Apis was considered a god; they treated the Apis Bull as royalty, giving it the best of everything.

The importance of the Apis Bull is highlighted in the book, *Egyptian Myth and Legend,* which says:

"Osiris was worshipped at Memphis in the form of the bull Apis, Egyptian Hapi, which was known to the Greeks as 'Serapis', their rendering of Asar-Hapi (Osiris-Apis). This sacred animal was reputed to be of miraculous birth, like the son of the Great Mother deity. 'It was begotten', Plutarch was informed, 'by a ray of generative light flowing from the moon.' 'Apis', said Herodotus, 'was a young black bull whose mother can have no other offspring.' It was known by its marks; it had 'on its forehead a white triangular spot, on its back an eagle, a beetle lump under its tongue, while the hair of its tail was double'. Plutarch said that 'on account of the great resemblance which the Egyptians imagine between Osiris and the moon, its more bright and shining parts being shadowed and obscured by those that are of a darker hue, they call the Apis the living image of Osiris'. The bull, Herodotus says, was 'a fair and beautiful image of the soul of Osiris'. Diodorus similarly states that Osiris manifested himself to men through successive ages as Apis. *The soul of Osiris migrated into this animal*', he explains."[43]

Now that we have a brief understanding of the Egyptian gods, let us look at two astronomical events and how they could have influenced the Egyptians.

In 1533 BC, the sun was located within the constellation of Taurus, the bull. The sun became totally eclipsed with the sun's

---

[43] Donald Mackenzie, Egyptian Myth and Legend (London: Gresham Publishing Company, 1907), p. 69-70.

corona visible between the bull's horns. The Egyptians would have seen this as a cosmic interaction between them and the constellation represented as the Apis Bull god. The total solar eclipse centered in Memphis, Egypt, and plunged them into darkness for about three minutes. The Apis Bull priest would have known the sun was between the horns of the constellation Taurus, the bull, at the eclipse moment. The sun's location is reminiscent of the Apis Bull god's statues with a sun disk between their horns. The implications of this event can be seen in the elevation of the Apis Bull within this timeframe. Shortly after the total solar eclipse, the station of the Apis Bull was elevated. This is evident in the archeological evidence. Within the early part of the 18th Dynasty of Egypt, the Apis Bull was built in an elaborate area attached to the temple for Osiris. Upon the death of the Apis Bull, it was entombed in an elaborate catacomb with a sarcophagus. The largest sarcophagus, weighing over nine tons, was found to contain an entire mummified Apis Bull.

The second astronomical event occurred in the first part of April 1524 BC and carries significance for Egypt. Fifteen days before the Exodus, the moon and Jupiter were visually obscured by the sun being reborn together. The last waning crescent moon was seen on March 31, 1524 BC, and the first crescent of the new moon was seen on April 2, 1524 BC. At the same time, Jupiter moved from an evening star on March 24, 1524 BC, to a morning star on April 7, 1524 BC. The rebirth of Jupiter and the moon at the same time meant that they were visually obstructed by the sun at the same time. The symbolical implication is that the deity Osiris is said to go from death to life, signified by Jupiter going from an evening star to a morning star. The rebirth of both the moon and Jupiter simultaneously came on the first few days of the same month as the Exodus. This is important because after many months of plagues initiated by God attempting to free Israel, the event in the perspective of Egyptian mythology was brought on.

On March 24, 1524 BC, Jupiter was an evening star representing Osiris living in the land of the dead. On April 1, 1524 BC, Jupiter, representing Osiris in the land of the dead and the moon representing his wife Isis, were visually obscured by the sun together. On April 2, 1524 BC, the first sighting of the moon occurred. On April 7, 1524 BC the first sight of Jupiter as a morning star occurred—which represented the birth of Horus, the son of Osiris and Isis.

The Egyptians would have noticed the double birth of Horus and Isis. The birth of Horus at the time of the plagues on Egypt would have been interpreted as their god Horus coming to save Egypt. This is based on the premise that Horus conquered chaos and restored peace. This belief hardened the Egyptians' hearts to Moses' message, despite all the plagues occurring. Both the moon and Jupiter were reborn simultaneously; this is significant, seeing that Jupiter represents Osiris and the moon represents Isis. The legend states that Osiris and Isis are husband and wife. Since they are a couple being reborn simultaneously, this would be significant to the Egyptians. The rebirth of both the moon and Jupiter at the same time is very rare and a truly momentous occasion.

Let us put this into the perspective of the Bible. Moses would be preparing the tribe of Israel for the last plague on Egypt. The Egyptians witnessed all the plagues, but after witnessing the rebirth of Osiris and Isis (in the stars) at the same time emboldened them. The Egyptians would have seen this rare double rebirth as a sign that their gods were on the Egyptians' side. The last plague on Egypt coincided with the Egyptian celebration of the birth of the god Horus who by legend is the first-born and only child of Osiris and Isis. Furthermore, within days, Moses proclaims death to all first-borns to include the gods' first-born son Horus.

To further understand the Egyptians' viewpoint, let us look at a possible sequence of events based on the evidence.

On May 9, 1533 BC, a total solar eclipse occurred just before sunset centering over Egypt's cities Thebes, and Memphis. The totality lasted about three minutes. Upon examination, they realized the solar eclipse occurred directly between the horns of the god Taurus. This total solar eclipse over Thebes and Memphis, Egypt, elevated the Apis Bull god on May 9, 1533 BC as seen in the archeological evidence of the eighteenth dynasty.

On April 1, 1524 BC, the moon and the planet Jupiter were reborn together signifying, that Osiris had moved from the land of the dead to the land of the living. Now that Osiris lived in the land of the living as the god Horus, he now can bring peace back to Egypt by taking on the Israelites' God. Moses met the challenge and declared the tenth plague on Egypt: "For I will go through the land of Egypt in that night, and will smite all the first-born in the land of Egypt, both man and beast; and against all the gods of Egypt" (Exodus 12:12). Moses declared the last plague to kill all the first-born to include the god Horus, the first-born son of Osiris.

121

Israel at the Time of the Exodus

The evening total solar eclipse of 1533 BC would have been obvious in Egypt. In May, the sun moved through Taurus the bull's horns when it entered into a total solar eclipse. The eclipse's totality was seen over most of Egypt to include the primary locations where Israel lived. Years later the sun was once again in the constellation of Taurus the bull during the crossing of the Red Sea in 1524 BC. These two events may have played a part in the children of Israel declaring the golden calf as their god.

On March 9, 1533 BC, the sun was moving through the horns of the bull constellation Taurus. At sunset, a total solar eclipse occurred between the horns of the constellation Taurus. The sun was in the constellation of Taurus, the bull, at the time of the burning bush and again at the Red Sea crossing. Israel would have seen that the Exodus occurred under the bull constellation and gave it credit for the Exodus. Israel would have believed that the Taurus bull was their protector in the wilderness. Furthermore, by the time they reach the land across the Red Sea, it would be again during the month marked by the Taurus bull constellation, giving further credibility to the Taurus bull. When Moses tried to explain that God had appeared to him in a burning bush, many of the Israelites would have thought it was instead the Taurus bull.

Israel's belief in the god Apis drove them to construct a golden calf shortly after reaching the valley at the base of God's mountain. The calf that they made was then declared to be their god and deliverer. Exodus 32:4 says, "made it a molten calf: and they said, these are thy gods, O Israel, which brought thee up out of the land of Egypt." This belief resurfaced hundreds of years later. "Whereupon the king took counsel, and made two calves of gold; and said unto them, It is too much for you to go up to Jerusalem: behold thy gods, O Israel, which brought thee up out of the land of Egypt. And he set the one in Bethel, and the other put he in Dan" (1 Kings 12:28-29).

It has been theorized that this golden calf has been the source of idol worship throughout Israel's early years. About this, Plunket states: "It has often been assumed that the golden calf set up and worshipped in the wilderness by the Israelites was a representation of the Apis god of Egypt; and that so also were the calves set up by Jeroboam in Bethel and in Dan on his return from Egypt."[44]

Maunder states in reference to Acts 7:41-42:

"If we turn to St. Stephen's reference to this occurrence, we find that he says, "And they made a calf in those days, and offered sacrifice unto the idol, and rejoiced in the works of their own hands. Then God turned, and gave them up to worship the host of heaven" (Acts 7:41-42).

In other words, their worship of the golden calf was star worship."[45]

---

[44] Emmeline M. Plunket, *Ancient Calendars and Constellations* (London: John Murray, 1903), p. 233.

[45] E. Walter Maunder, The Astronomy of the Bible: An Elementary Commentary on the Astronomical References of Holy Scripture (London: T. Sealey Clark & Co.) p. 193.

Maunder goes on to state:

> "It is probable that the 'golden calf,' worshipped by the Israelites in the wilderness, and, after the disruption, at Bethel and at Dan, was none other than an attempt to worship Jehovah under the symbol of Taurus, the leader of the zodiac and cognizance of the tribe of Joseph; regarded as a type of Him Who had been the leader of the people out of Egypt, and the Giver of the blessings associated with the return of the sun to Taurus, the revival of nature in spring-time. It was intended as a worship of Jehovah; it was in reality dire rebellion against Him, and a beginning of the worship of 'Mazzaloth and the heavenly host;' an idolatry that was bound to bring other idolatries."[46]

Israel observed the Taurus Bull eclipse and then witnessed the Exodus from the land of Egypt all occurring during the month of Taurus the bull. Israel then linked their deliverance to the Apis Bull god instead of giving credit to the true God.

Moses

The future was changed the moment God communed with Moses. Without this event, Moses might never have gone back to Egypt. This part will examine the impact of the total solar eclipse on Moses.

---

[46] Ibid, p. 252-253.

Moses' Location

The location where God communed with Moses is recorded in Exodus 3:1, which states, "Now Moses was keeping the flock of Jethro his father-in-law, the priest of Midian: and he led the flock to the backside of the wilderness, and came to the mountain of God, unto Horeb."

Moses' Timing

The timing of the event when God spoke to Moses through the burning bush had to occur before the Exodus from Egypt in 1524 BC.[47] The burning bush would have occurred in the desert before Moses returned to Egypt; the exact time is unknown.

The Old Testament does not tell us how old Moses was when he left Egypt the first time or how much time passed between the burning bush to the Exodus, but it does tell us how old he was at the Exodus. Moses informs us that he left Egypt "when Moses was grown up" (Exodus 2:11). This is the only age-related timing Moses provides for his first departure from Egypt. Moses' age is not recorded in the Old Testament when God appeared to him in the burning bush. The Bible tells us Moses first went before the Pharaoh of Egypt at 80 years of age (Exodus 7:7). The Old Testament does not tell us how much time elapsed between the burning bush and the Exodus from Egypt, just that it occurred before the Exodus from Egypt in 1524 BC.

---

[47] Jeffrey Grimm, *Solar Eclipses in the Bible* (United States: Jeffrey Grimm2021), appendices A and B.

Moses does not provide his age at the first departure from Egypt. The timing for his first departure from Egypt occurred "when Moses was grown up" (Exodus 2:11); this statement is repeated in Hebrews 11:24. Since this is not an age, many have theorized that this may be a level of education. This can be seen by comparing the following two verses:

Exodus 2:11 – "And it came to pass in those days, when Moses was grown up, that he went out unto his brethren, and looked on their burdens."

Acts 7:22-23 – "And Moses was instructed in all the wisdom of the Egyptians; and he was mighty in his words and works. But when he was well-nigh forty years old, it came into his heart to visit his brethren the children of Israel."

Moses' own words about himself were "when Moses was grown up," but (Acts 7:22-23) turns it into "Moses was instructed in all the wisdom of the Egyptians; and he was mighty in his words and works. But when he was well-nigh forty years old." By comparing the two verses, the statement, "when Moses was grown up," is expanded into extensive education and the exact age of 40 years old.

Stephen, quoted by Luke in Acts 7:23-32, stated Moses was 40 years old when he exited Egypt and 40 years later witnessed the burning bush. From the time of Moses to the time of Stephen's statement, over 1,500 years have elapsed. The early history of Israel has no sum of years for Moses leaving Egypt to the burning bush and the additional time to the Exodus. But the New Testament, Acts 7:23-32, gives his exact years.

The Bible does not inform us how Stephen gets to the two sets of 40 years. There are three possible options of how Stephen arrived at these numbers:

1. The Holy Spirit was prophesying through him
2. Non-written verbal history
3. Theological arrangement

The Holy Spirit Was Prophesying Through Stephen

Prophesying typically occurs when the Holy Spirit speaks about future information. Rarely does prophesy provide past event information. Also, typically, when the Holy Spirit speaks, the writer tells us that the Holy Spirit is doing so. However, just because it is written in the Bible does not mean that the Holy Spirit wrote or spoke it.

The Bible is written by imperfect people but inspired by the Holy Spirit unless stated that the Holy Spirit said it. The Bible often records accurately what people said or did, regardless if they were correct in word or action. Stephen said 40 years, so that is what was recorded. His words were recorded, not the validity of those words. The result of people writing or saying things shows a variance in information inside, meaning individuals wrote it based on their own knowledge—knowledge that could be inaccurate.

If the Holy Spirit inspired Stephen, a variation could have occurred in this verse. The Holy Spirit's inspiration allows for variations in the Bible by writers inspired by the Holy Spirit. An example of this inspiration that creates variance is to survey the sign placed over Jesus' cross.

1. Matthew states, "THIS IS JESUS THE KING OF THE JEWS." (Matthew 27:37)
2. Mark states, "THE KING OF THE JEWS." (Mark 15:26)
3. Luke states, "THIS IS THE KING OF THE JEWS." (Luke 23:38)
4. John states, "JESUS OF NAZARETH, THE KING OF THE JEWS." (John 19:19)

The sign only said one thing, not four different things. The fact that four different variations are given could be considered a contradiction. This must have been the apostles speaking because when the Holy Spirit speaks, He never contradicts Himself.

Luke does not inform us that the Holy Spirit was speaking or that Stephen was prophesying, so one is led to believe he was speaking from his own experience and understanding. Stephen's commentary is probably not a prophecy to rewrite the record of Moses. Stephen gave what appears to be a consolidated theological study of Israel's past that did not seek to clarify past events but rather shed light on current events. The purpose of the dialog in question was to present a quick summary of the Old Testament to emphasize that Scripture pointed to Jesus' arrival—something which those stoning Stephen failed to recognize.

With no indication that the Holy Spirit is speaking at this exact moment, the event appeared to be more scholarly than prophetic. It is probable that the exact years of 40 were not inspired as an exact truth from the Holy Spirit but instead imparted to us by the personal knowledge of Stephen.

Theological Study

Stephen's address was to the high priest and was not so interested in redefining history as much as pointing out the failure to recognize Jesus. The priests, scribes, and elders were knowledgeable in the Old Testament; they needed no education as to the past. Stephen ends his brief survey of the Old Testament with a transition to the New Testament, informing them that they killed the one who was prophesied to come to them.

Seeing the conversation with the high priest was a theological study, not a timeline study, one can conclude that the 40 years is more in line with theological symmetry. The idea behind the forty-year intervals could be Moses' 120 years of life divided into three equal parts. The first 40 years were for learning Egypt's ways, the second 40 years would be seeking God in the desert, and the last 40 years would be leading Israel through the wilderness. These three sets of 40 carry significance, seeing 40 is a religious number of completion and divine wholeness. One can cluster pivotal times in Moses' life, but at the same time, the actual years may not necessarily have added up to exactly 40 years; they could be a few years off.

Nonwritten and Verbal History/Tradition

The theological study of Moses could have been the result of a verbal tradition at the time of Stephen's address. Several Bible commentators agree that this may have been a nonverbal tradition:

Clarke's Commentary – "This was a general tradition among the Jews: Moses was 40 years in Pharaoh's court, 40 years in Midian, and 40 years he served Israel."[48]

Matthew Poole's Commentary – "Forty years old; this age of Moses is not set down in his history, but they might have it by tradition, which is here confirmed unto us by the holy penman: these forty years Moses spent in Pharaoh's court."[49]

Gill's Exposition of the Entire Bible – "This Stephen had from tradition, and not from Scripture, which is silent about the age of Moses at this time...twenty years old was Moses at that time; and there are that say, that he was forty years old. And elsewhere still more particularly; Moses was 'forty' years in the palace of Pharaoh, forty years in Midian, (the Amsterdam edition reads, 'in the wilderness', wrongly,) and he served Israel forty years.' Indeed, the fabulous history of his life makes him to be but fifteen years of age at this time."[50]

The Old Testament is silent about Moses' lengths of the years in Egypt and the wilderness. A reasonable conclusion would be that the two 40-years references must have been from a tradition. The revelation occurred 1,500 years later and with no

---

[48] Adam Clarke, *The New Testament: A Commentary and Critical Notes* (New York: Myers, 1835), p. 358.

[49] Peter Vinke continuation of Matthew Poole's Commentary, *Annotations upon the Holy Bible*.

[50] John Gill, An Exposition of the New Testament, 1746-1748.

indication of the Holy Spirit speaking. The Old Testament states that Moses was 80 years old, so it is reasonable to say that Moses witnessed the burning bush sometime before his 80ᵗʰ year, whether it be that same year or multiple years before that.

A second timing tradition: to be evaluated is the length of time from the moment Moses witnessed the burning bush to Israel's departure from Egypt. Moses does not provide a timetable for the events starting with the burning bush to the Exodus from Egypt. Over the last 3,500 years, well-meaning historians have added layers of theological dust over the Scripture so that when we view this event, we view it through the theological dust. The timing from the burning bush to the Exodus is a length of time distorted by that theological dust.

Nowhere in the Old Testament are we informed that Moses saw a burning bush and then ran to Egypt, resulting in a quick Exodus. However, historians and even Hollywood movies depict Moses immediately running to Egypt and bringing down the ten plagues after encountering the burning bush. The theological dust over this Scripture is so thick that the moment one thinks burning bush, one thinks running to Egypt with a quick Exodus. The fact is that there is no timeframe given in the Bible. The Old Testament does not state that Moses ran immediately to Egypt after witnessing the burning bush. The Bible also does not say that the Exodus occurred in short order after the burning bush. The Old Testament is silent to the length of time from the burning bush to the Exodus.

The fact is that many things occurred between Exodus 3:2 and Exodus 12:31. While Moses does not provide the lapsing time from the burning bush to the Exodus, he provides a chronology of things that occurred. By examining the events that occurred from the burning bush to the Exodus, we can set aside the theological dust that has accumulated over the Scripture and examine it as it is.

1. Moses was in the back of the desert tending Jethro's sheep on the back of the mountain (Exodus 3:1).

2. When God came to Moses in the burning bush, Moses had many excuses (Exodus 3:2-17).

   - Moses did not consider himself worthy enough. God told Moses not to worry for He would be with him.
   - Moses argued that the people might not believe that God appeared to him. So, God performed several miracles for Moses, such as staff to snake and making his hand turn to leprosy.
   - Moses argued that he was not an elegant speaker, so God told Moses that he could use his brother Aaron.

3. As a result of the excuses, "the anger of Jehovah was kindled against Moses" (Exodus 4:14).

4. Moses left the backside of the mountains and returned to his father-in-law in Midian. The exact location that Moses saw the burning bush is not known. However, if we use the traditionally excepted site for Mount Sinai in the Sinai Peninsula, it is about 200 miles overland to Midian. If Moses had stayed with the sheep, the travel

would have been slow and time-consuming (Exodus 4:18).

5. Upon returning, Moses said to Jethro, "Let me go, I pray thee, and return unto my brethren that are in Egypt, and see whether they be yet alive" (Exodus 4:18). Jethro told Moses, "Go in peace."

6. God communicated with Moses a second time. After Jethro told Moses he could go, God again told Moses, "Go, return into Egypt; for all the men are dead that sought thy life" (Exodus 4:21-23).

7. Moses decided to take his wife and son to Egypt (Exodus 4:24).

8. On the road to Egypt, Moses went to "the lodging-place" (Exodus 4:24). The lodging-place is not specified. However, it is probably at the location that Moses saw the burning bush and likely the spot that Aaron met Moses. If true, then Moses going to the Mountain of God indicates that he did not go directly to Egypt as God requested.

9. At the lodging-place, God met Moses and "sought to kill him" (Exodus 4:24).

10. Zipporah circumcised their son (Exodus4:25-26).

11. God said to Aaron, "Go into the wilderness to meet Moses" (Exodus 4:27). The moment God spoke with Aaron and his departure from Egypt to find Moses is not known. Aaron may have left at the exact moment Moses

saw the burning bush or at a later time. However, the events listed in Exodus chapter 4 notates it in the timeline so it is relayed as such here.

12. Aaron left Egypt at God's command and went to Moses at the Mountain of God. the Bible does not state how long it took for Aaron to go from Egypt to Moses. (Exodus 4:27).

13. "Moses told Aaron all the words of Jehovah wherewith he had sent him, and all the signs wherewith he had charged him" (Exodus 4:28).

14. Moses and Aaron then go to Egypt together (Exodus 4:29).

15. Once in Egypt, "Moses and Aaron went and gathered together all the elders of the children of Israel" (Exodus 4:29). Moses hints that persuading the Israelites to follow him was difficult and maybe alluding to additional time from his arrival in Egypt before going to the Pharaoh in order to persuade Israel: "Moses spoke before Jehovah, saying, Behold, the children of Israel have not hearkened unto me" (Exodus 6:12). The time to gather together all the elders of the children of Israel and convince them to follow Moses may have taken a lot of time.

Note: Exodus chapters 5 to 12 cover the events of Pharaoh resisting God and the subsequent plagues on Egypt. Pharaoh most likely lived in Thebes seeing it was the political capital of Egypt. Moses most likely lived with the Israelites in lower Egypt. Every time Moses went before Pharaoh, a potential 100-mile round trip to and from Thebes Egypt possibly occurred. Additionally, most of the durations of time between each plague are not known.

16. Moses went before the Pharaoh in Exodus 5:1 indicating the first potential 100-mile round trip to and from Pharaoh.

17. Officers of the children of Israel came and cried out to the Pharaoh in Exodus 5:15. This would require the officers to make a one-way journey, potentially of more than 50 miles.

18. When they came out from the Pharaoh, "they met Moses and Aaron, who stood in the way, as they came forth from Pharaoh" (Exodus 5:20). This may indicate a potential 100-mile round trip for Moses and Aaron to meet the officers.

19. Moses and Aaron made arrangements to meet with the Pharaoh, then they may have had a waiting time before seeing Pharaoh. "Pharaoh also called the wise men and the sorcerers" (Exodus 7:11) with no indication if they had to travel there or not.

20. Seven days after the first plague on Egypt started, God told Moses to return to Pharaoh (Exodus 7:25).

21. Exodus 8:8 has Pharaoh calling for Moses and Aaron, indicating a possible 100-mile round trip plus time for the Pharaoh's message to get to him.

22. No interaction between Moses and the Pharaoh is recorded for the third plague.

23. Moses receives another request from God to go talk to Pharaoh: "Jehovah said unto Moses, Rise up early in the morning, and stand before Pharaoh; lo he cometh forth to the water" (Exodus 8:20).

24. Then Pharaoh called for Moses in Exodus 8:25 indicating the potential for a 100-mile round trip plus time for the Pharaoh's message to get to him.

25. A three-day journey into the desert and sacrifice to the Lord (Exodus 8:27-28).

26. Moses went before Pharaoh and the fifth plague started the next morning (Exodus 9:1-6). Moses potentially had to perform another 100-mile round trip.

27. "Pharaoh sent, and, behold, there was not so much as one of the cattle of the Israelites dead" (Exodus 9:7). At Pharaoh's command, someone may have had to travel over hundreds of miles to verify this information.

28. Moses went before Pharaoh and the sixth plague started (Exodus 9:8-12). Moses potentially had to perform another 100-mile round trip.

29. The seventh plague of hail struck all the land of Egypt except where Israel was living. The Bible does not state how or if Pharaoh knew this, but he summoned Moses (Exodus 9:13-27). This again, indicated the potential for a 100-mile round trip plus time for the Pharaoh's message to get to him.

30. God sent Moses back to Pharaoh before the eighth plague of locusts (Exodus 10:1-20). Indicating the potential for a 100-mile round trip plus time for Pharaoh's message to get to him.

31. After the ninth plague, Pharaoh called for Moses (Exodus 10:24). Indicating the potential for a 100-mile round trip plus time for Pharaoh's message to get to him.

32. Tenth plague with subsequent Exodus from Egypt.

The theological dust covering the burning bush is so thick that when one thinks of the burning bush, they think of Moses running to Egypt, resulting in ten rapid-fire plagues and all Israel exits Egypt. Ussher demonstrates the level of theological dust covering this length of time. Ussher placed the burning bush around January 1, 1491 BC, and the Exodus from Egypt four months later on May 5, 1491 BC. Usher provides only four months for all the events from the burning bush to Exodus. Ussher is even more specific on his beliefs for the ten plagues as he states: "The Jews saw a whole years space, at several intervals of time; whereas indeed they were all sent within one month."[51] Ussher acknowledges that the Jews have a tradition that the ten plagues lasted one year. However, Ussher canceled the Jew's tradition with a newer tradition by declaring "indeed" all ten plagues occurred within one month. The tradition of inserting a short span of time into this nonreported span of time brings a risk of imposing our own beliefs and traditions on the Bible.

---

[51] James Ussher, *The Annuals of the World* (London: Tyler, 1658), p. 13.

About traditions within worship, Jesus stated: "But in vain do they worship me, teaching as their doctrines and precepts of men. Ye leave the commandment of God, and hold fast the tradition of men. And he said unto them, full well do ye reject the commandment of God, that ye may keep your tradition" (Mark 7:7-8). As students of the Bible, we should be fast to speak where the Bible speaks and not bind the Bible by manmade traditions. When the Bible does not specify a length of time then neither should we do so based solely on tradition.

The Bible is silent about the time; however, it is not silent about events. The Old Testament does not provide the length of time from Moses leaving Egypt the first time to the burning bush. The Bible also does not provide the length of time from the burning bush to Moses' arrival in Egypt with the subsequent Exodus. When evaluating the recorded chronology of Exodus chapters 3 through 12, one can see that more time versus less time is needed. The Bible provides a chronology of events that hints there could be many years between the burning bush and the Exodus from Egypt.

Moses' Burning Bush

Moses was tending to his father-in-law's work for many years. Moses met Jethro's daughter, Zipporah, shortly after exiting Egypt and worked for Jethro until he returned to Egypt to save Israel. The Old Testament is silent about the years Moses worked for Jethro, but the New Testament gives 40 years.

At this time, Moses witnessed the burning bush.

Moses and the burning bush story is among the most told stories from the Old Testament and likely one of the first Bible school lessons taught to young children. Teachers tell children the story and then show an image of a bush consumed by fire. The repetitive reinforcements of the image of a bush fully consumed by fire cements the view as fact for them. Through repetitive retellings of this story, children become conditioned to associate this image with Moses' burning bush. They are taught it was a natural bush that was entirely consumed yet not being consumed by natural fire. The illustration and story are presented so often that it becomes easy to become complacent with the story. By the time one becomes an adult, they have become conditioned to envision a bush entirely consumed by fire yet does not turn to ash.

Many have become so complacent with the story that they fail to see the miracle of the event itself. They further accommodate the story by failing to see all the contradictions of nature that caused Moses to say, "I will now turn aside, and see this great sight, why the bush is not burnt." Many have a hard time recognizing the miracle of the contradiction that made this a "great sight."

A deeper understanding of the event will be gained by closely examining the event as recorded by Moses (the eyewitness of the event).

Exodus 3:2-3 – "The angel of Jehovah appeared unto him in a flame of fire out of the midst of a bush: and he looked, and, behold, the bush burned with fire, and the bush was not consumed. And Moses said, I will now turn aside, and see this great sight, why the bush is not burnt."

Moses' statement that the "bush burned with fire" makes us think the bush was engulfed in a fire to the point one sees only a ball of flames. This view matches what naturally occurs to bushes that are on fire. An example of this is when a Christmas tree catches on fire; there are but a few seconds before the entire tree turns into a ball of flames. The same goes for a bush once it catches on fire; it is instantaneously consumed by flames causing the bush not to be visible behind a ball of flames.

Moses continued the description, "The bush was not consumed." The definition of consumed would mean to devourer, swallow, and make disappear. The natural consumption of a bush by fire occurs in two ways. First, the entire bush visually disappears behind a wall of flames. The flames will be so plentiful and bright that the bush itself is no longer visible. The second aspect of a bush being consumed by fire is its turning to ash. The fire stops when the entire bush has been consumed and turned into ash. The statement, "the bush was not consumed," creates a contradiction to nature's laws making this a miracle. In the perspective of Moses' statement that the "bush burned with fire," the laws of nature would imply that the bush was consumed by the flames both visually and materially.

Moses' statements can be broken down in two ways:

1. First possible visualization:
   - The "bush burned with fire" means the bush is fully consumed visually by flames to the point it is a ball of flames.
   - "The bush was not consumed" might mean the fire did not materially consume the leaves and branches into ash.

2. Second possible visualization:
   - The "bush burned with fire" might mean the flames radiated away from the bush but did not obstruct the viewing of the bush for the bush was not visually consumed by flames.
   - "The bush was not consumed" could mean the fire did not consume the bush both visually, as in blocking the view through total fire consumption, and materially consumed, as in the leaves and branches did not turn into ash.

The first possible visualization of Moses' burning bush image is the popular Sunday school rendition of the burning bush. The burning bush is visualized as fully consumed by fire. However, Moses added that "the bush was not consumed" explaining that the bush's leaves and branches were not turned to ash. The dilemma comes when Moses states that "the bush was not consumed." He did not say it was only visually consumed but that it was not also materially consumed. Moses did not single out only one of the two forms of a natural consumption of a bush by fire. Making this assumption on our own is not staying true to Moses' description.

The second possible visualization of Moses' burning bush image is in line with a strict following of the description. This visualization has a bush that has fire radiating out away from the bush. The bush itself has no flames immediately on it, making it not consumed by fire both visually and materially.

One can conclude that Moses' two contradicting observations are intended to describe the event as one observation. Making both statements to be one statement, one could say the bush had no flames on it, but the flames could be seen around its perimeter. Combining the two statements into one statement makes a description of the event. It is a fire burning around the bush but did not touch the bush.

This description also matches Moses' reason for turning aside to "see the great sight, why the bush is not burnt." Moses' decision is understandable for he was shepherding a flock at this time, and he would want to inspect everything for safety. What makes this turning aside so different from any other is the reason for doing so. Moses declared this burning bush a "great sight." This expression would typically be used in reference to something out of the ordinary and unexpected. Moses would have been familiar with fire and most likely would not declare fire a "great sight" unless there was something unusual about it. Moses then tells us that "the bush is not burnt." The great sight that caused Moses to turn aside was a bush that was not burnt. This raises the question: which description of the burning bush better matches Moses' reason for turning aside? Is it an entirely visually consumed bush by flames but, after looking at it for a while, noticed it was not being consumed? Or is it a bush that has flames radiating away from it but has no flames immediately on it, making it not burned at all? Which statement is more aligned with Moses' words?

Now let us look at the last part of Moses' description, which is actually the first part: "The angel of Jehovah appeared unto him in a flame of fire out of the midst of a bush" (Exodus 3:2).

First, let us understand the difference between fire and flame. *Fire* is the rapid oxidation resulting from combustion. *Flame* is a glowing gas made by the fire's rapid oxidation. This means the fire is the source of the flames and a fire would consist of thousands of flames but with only one fire. Applying this to Moses' description, the bush would be the object experiencing the fire (rapid oxidation). The fire (rapid oxidation) produced gas, seen as glowing gases called flames. The flames last as long as it takes for the gas to be consumed and then disappear, making room for the next flame to explode outward. A burning bush would have thousands of flames emitting from it.

Moses informs us that "the angel of Jehovah appeared unto him." Moses states the angel "appeared." This would imply that Moses saw the angel. This raises the question: did the angel leave the burning bush and stay with Moses for a time or was the angel inseparable from the bush?

Moses further states that the angel appeared "in a flame of fire out of the midst of a bush." This describes how the angel appeared unto Moses. Recall that fire is the process of rapid oxidation that produces gases that are visible as flames. The flames that are produced are short lived. Seeing Moses described the angel that appeared to him in a flame that came out of the bush, we can conclude that the angel left the bush with a spectacular flash that Moses called a flame. Since Moses referred to it as a flame in a singular fashion, one would conclude that this flame stood out above all the others in magnitude and brightness.

In addition, for Moses to call it a flame, it would be short-lived. Since the flame left the bush and we are told the flame came out of the midst of the bush, we can conclude that the angel was not bound to the bush but rather independent of the bush. Moses further clarifies this in one of his last writings before he died. In Deuteronomy 33:16, Moses speaks of this angel in which he said, "Him that dwelt in the bush." Moses informs us that the angel dwelt in the bush not that the angel was the bush. The phrase "dwelt in" implies that the bush and angel are not the same being but separate and independent. Since the angel was not substantially bound to the bush, the bush could theoretically leave and the angel could still be there seeing that they are separate. If this were the case, one could say the angel came out of the bush in the form of a flame then stayed with Moses. Theoretically, the angel could have stayed longer than the bush since the two beings are separate and independent. However, Moses brings our attention back to the bush by writing, "God called unto him out of the midst of the bush" (Exodus 3:4). This verse now places God inside the bush seeing a voice came out from the midst of the bush. This raises the question: is the angel in the flame God? Or are they separate individuals? If they were separate individuals, then both the angel of the Lord and God would have been present. If they were the same individual, He must have gone back into the burning bush after appearing.

Moses' description of the burning bush is suggestive of the total solar eclipse that passed over the Sinai Peninsula. A total solar eclipse occurred around sunset on May 9, 1533 BC. The eclipse's altitude would be a few degrees off the horizon. Anyone in the mountain range who viewed the solar eclipse would have seen it just over the mountain tops. The mountains could obstruct part of the eclipse's bottom, giving the impression that the eclipse is setting on the mountain. At the moment when the sun's corona became visible, a phenomenon known as the diamond ring effect occurred. This phenomenon would have appeared to Moses as a flame of fire shooting out from the bush lasting less than a minute. The paralleling of the angel with the burning bush and the total solar eclipse will demonstrate the similarities of the event.

On the evening of May 9, 1533 BC, at about 6:20 PM, the sun was setting for the day. Thirty minutes from setting, the sun went into a total solar eclipse. The eclipse was centered over the length of the Sinai Peninsula. Anyone in the Sinai Peninsula or surrounding area would have witnessed this eclipse. If the individual were in the mountains, the mountains would have obstructed some of the eclipse. If only partial obstruction of the eclipse had occurred, it would have been the bottom portion due to the mountains. The eclipse would then look as if it sat on the mountain. The eclipse of the sun at sunset looked like a burning bush. Totality started with a flame exploding out from the center of the eclipse. It was on this flame that the angel of Jehovah used to appear to Moses. This exploding flame that always occurs at the start of every total solar eclipse is called the diamond ring effect. The center of the eclipse was dark, like the silhouette of a bush. The area around the silhouette would be radiating flames that we know were the sun's corona. With the total solar eclipse occurring so low on the horizon, there would be a substantial amount of the earth's atmosphere that the light would have to pass through, resulting in a glowing red corona. The resulting event would appear to be a bush that was not consumed both visually and materially yet had fire radiating out from it. The eclipse lasted about three minutes and then was gone.

The night Moses witnessed the burning bush is paralleled in the last plague on Egypt:

Exodus 12:5-13 – "Your lamb shall be without blemish, a male a year old: ye shall take it from the sheep, or from the goats: and ye shall keep it until the fourteenth day of the same month; and the whole assembly of the congregation of Israel shall kill it at evening. And they shall take of the blood, and put it on the two side-posts and on the lintel, upon the houses wherein they shall eat it. And they shall eat the flesh in that night, roast with fire, and unleavened bread; and with bitter herbs they shall eat it. Eat not of it raw, nor boiled at all with water, but roast with fire; its head with his legs and with the inwards thereof. And ye shall let nothing of it remain until the morning; but that which remaineth of it until the morning ye shall burn with fire. And thus shall ye eat it: with your loins girded, your shoes on your feet, and your staff in your hand; and ye shall eat it in haste: it is Jehovah's Passover. For I will go through the land of Egypt in that night, and will smite all the first-born in the land of Egypt, both man and beast; and against all the gods of Egypt I will execute judgments: I am the Lord. And the blood shall be to you for a token upon the houses where ye are: and when I see the blood, I will

---

pass over you, and there shall no plague be upon you to destroy you, when I smite the land of Egypt."

It is important to note that many Israelites were shepherds. The primary responsibility of the shepherd is the health and well-being of the flock. The shepherds would protect the sheep from predators such as wolves and lions. The shepherds would protect the sheep from dangers such as drop-offs. The shepherd led the flock to water and food. For their hard work, shepherds received clothes and food from the sheep as relayed to us by the *Dictionary of the Bible*:

> The skin of a sheep, roughly tanned with all the wool on, is the common winter jacket of a shepherd or peasant. To kill a sheep or lamb for a stranger's meal is one of the first acts of Bedouin hospitality. In the country, sheep are killed only in such circumstances or in honor of some festive occasion.[52]

The *Dictionary of the Bible* points out that the shepherds kill their sheep using the wool-covered skins to make jackets and meat for nourishment. The killing of a sheep occurred for two primary reasons: first as hospitality for a stranger and second in honor of a festive occasion.

Assuming these hospitalities were the same as they are today, then Moses would have followed such customs and courtesies. Seeing the flock did not belong to Moses but to his father-in-law, Jethro, Moses would have been representing him in all that

---

[52] James Hastings. *Dictionary of the Bible* (New York: Charles Scribner's Sons, 1909), p. 844.

he did. Moses would have wanted to follow the customs and courtesies when tending the flock, especially seeing his actions reflected on his father-in-law. Moses ' obligation was to kill a lamb if a stranger came for dinner or a festive occasion was called for.

The Bible is silent about what if anything Moses ate that night, but it is reasonable to conclude that Moses ate a lamb. Moses stated, "The angel of Jehovah appeared unto him in a flame of fire out of the midst of a bush" (Exodus 3:2). Since the angel could be classified as a stranger, then he would be expected to kill a sheep if not to feed the angel but at the very least in their honor. Moses could have also seen the angel of Jehovah and the burning bush as a reason for a festive occasion in the angel's honor. Both of these views could have been justifiable for the killing of a sheep for dinner that night. Regardless, Moses had the ability and responsibility of killing and eating a lamb if the circumstances required it. One would imagine that the night Moses saw the burning bush would be no exception. Just think; if customs called for the killing and eating of a sheep but Moses refused to do so for the angel of the Lord's arrival, how would that reflect on Moses and his father-in-law Jethro?

The Passover can be paralleled with the night God spoke to Moses in the burning bush. Six parallels can be seen between these two nights.

1. Parallel one

    - *Passover night*: A lamb was to be sacrificed on the night of the Passover.
    - *Moses in the desert*: This is the animal that Moses was shepherding when he witnessed the burning

bush. Seeing Moses had lambs around him shows he had the means to eat a lamb the night he witnessed the burning bush.

2. Parallel two

- *Passover night*: The lamb was to be cooked over a fire with no water.
- *Moses in the desert*: When Moses was in the desert, he would have had little to no water, so cooking over a fire with no water would be the most likely way he cooked his meal.

3. Parallel three

- *Passover night*: The Passover lamb was to be cooked whole.
- *Moses in the desert*: Moses would not have gutted a lamb with no way to wash up after, so he would have cooked it whole.

4. Parallel four

- *Passover night*: The Passover feast involved unleavened bread with bitter herbs.
- *Moses in the desert*: Both unleavened bread and bitter herbs could have been easily used in the desert by Moses.

5. Parallel five

- *Passover night*: The lamb was killed before sunset and the blood was immediately painted on the doorframe but not on the door, giving the appearance that the door was on fire but not consumed.
- *Moses in the desert*: Just before sunset Moses witnessed the total solar eclipse that appeared to be a bush on fire but not consumed.

6. Parallel six

- *Passover night*: Throughout the night, Israel ate the Passover meal. They were in the door that was painted to appear as if on fire but not consumed.
- *Moses in the desert*: Witnessed the total solar eclipse that appeared to be a bush on fire but not consumed, and by witnessing this bush that was not consumed, Moses witnessed "him that dwelt in the bush."

Moses would have noticed the eclipse before sunset and then killed and cooked the lamb for dinner. Moses would have seen the total solar eclipse just before sunset, matching the timing requirement of the blood being painted on the doors in Egypt just before sunset. Painting the doorframe and not the door would have looked like a door on fire that was not consumed. Not painting the baseboards would give the appearance that the door was sitting on the ground. This would look a lot like a painting of the burning bush that was not consumed. It also looked similar to a total solar eclipse that occurred just above the mountains. The eclipse had a burning red corona and a blacked-out center that was not on fire. The painting of blood around the doors would look similar to the solar eclipse with the bottom portion of the corona blocked by the mountain tops. Finally, the parallel of the door that was not consumed by fire used to conceal the children of Israel is much like the bush that was not consumed that concealed the angel of Jehovah.

Moses was in the desert by a mountain when he communed with God. Moses was in the Sinai Peninsula for many years, possibly over 40 years. Setting the Exodus year at 1524 BC would place Moses in the mountains of Sinai at 1533 BC. Placing Moses in the Sinai desert at the time of the total solar eclipse would mean Moses most likely witnessed the eclipse. Moses would have seen this eclipse occurring on the top of a mountain, giving the appearance of a burning bush. Moses then describes a burning bush that behaved the same way as the totality of the solar eclipse. Moses paralleled the night God delivered Israel from Egypt with the night God told Moses to free Israel from Egypt through the mandate that everyone paint their doors to look like the solar eclipse's totality. This parallel further confirms the conclusion that Moses witnessed the total solar eclipse. Seeing that Moses witnessed an event that meets the requirements set in Scripture, it would be irresponsible to ignore the fact and not associate the eclipse with the burning bush described in the Bible.

Conclusion

God gave Egypt, Israel, and Moses a choice to believe in God or not to believe in God. In the Exodus story, three parties are identified: the Egyptians, Israel, and Moses. The three parties of the Exodus believed that a god was responsible for the events; however, the three parties could not agree on which god was responsible. After the Egyptians witnessed the birth of Horus the son of Osiris at the same time of Isis' birth, they believed their god Horus was coming to save them. After Israel saw the total solar eclipse within the bull's horns and the Exodus from Egypt, Israel believed the Apis bull god saved them. After Moses experienced the total solar eclipse in the form of a burning bush, Moses believed the Exodus was because of Israel's God. Moses chose to give God credit for everything.

9

Conclusion

Early patriarchs of the Bible witnessed God's power in heavenly phenomena. Moses and King David believed the day and night sky were ways God communed with them. Moses gave us his thoughts on the stars: "God said, Let there be lights in the firmament of heaven to divide the day from the night; and let them be for signs" (Genesis 1:14). King David made a song highlighting the religious view of the sky: "The heavens declare the glory of God; And the firmament showeth his handiwork. Day unto day uttereth speech, And night unto night showeth knowledge. There is no speech nor language; Their voice is not heard. Their line is gone out through all the earth, And their words to the end of the world. In them hath he set a tabernacle for the sun" (Psalm 19:1-4). Furthermore, Amos credits the creation of constellations, star clusters, and total solar eclipses to God: "Seek him that maketh the Pleiades and Orion, and turneth the shadow of death into the morning, and maketh the day dark with night" (Amos 5:8).

God knew everything before time began, so God could have built into the fabric of creation the events at the exact time and location needed for the person requiring the miracle. This view does not demand that the miracle method cannot ever be discovered or understood but instead focuses on God's choice to provide a miracle for the people who needed it.

The first part of this book covered four examples of God using solar eclipses to communicate with His people. The four Eclipses occurred for Job, King Solomon, Deborah, and Gideon. These four individuals were at specific locations at specific times that line up with solar eclipses. The individual described this unknown event from the perspective of their understanding at the time. The four eclipses highlight the fact that God used solar eclipses as a method to communicate His desire.

The Story of Job

Job's conversation with God included a solar eclipse that Job witnessed. Historians know Job lived in an area that experienced the annular eclipse at the time he was alive. Job confirms that he saw the solar eclipse with his description of this specific eclipse's unique characteristics: "Let them curse it that curse the day, who are ready to rouse up leviathan. Let the stars of the twilight thereof be dark: Let it look for light, but have none; Neither let it behold the eyelids of the morning" (Job 3:8-9). Job described a solar eclipse at evening time when the sun was in the vicinity of Hydra constellation referred to as leviathan.

King Solomon's Ten Tribes Torn Away

God communicated to King Solomon and all Israel with a solar eclipse. The year before King Solomon died was marked by a solar eclipse. Bible historians have pinpointed the year of King Solomon's death and know he was in Jerusalem in the year leading up to his death. Astronomy has also proven that a solar eclipse occurred in the sky over Jerusalem in the last year of his life. King Solomon described a solar eclipse in these verses: "Before the sun, and the light, and the moon, and the stars, are darkened" (Ecclesiastes 12:2) and "before the silver cord is loosed" (Ecclesiastes 12:6). King Solomon described the solar eclipse as the sun, moon, and stars growing dark. Then King Solomon tells us that at the moment of the year when the sun moved into the life-giving water stream of the constellation Aquarius referred to as the silver cord, the sun went dark, severing the silver cord. This exactly describes the eclipse he witnessed!

Judge Deborah

God's prophetic battle in the stars paved the way for Israel's fight against their oppressors. Judge Deborah lived "between Ramah and Beth-el in the hill-country of Ephraim" (Judges 4:5). On October 30, 1207 BC, Deborah witnessed the solar eclipse around the head of the constellation Scorpius that is in the form of a scorpion. The constellation Sagittarius is among the scorpion constellation; this war that occurred in the stars with the archer killing the scorpion would be connected with Israel's defeat of their enemies and the death of the enemy general Sisera. "From heaven fought the stars, from their courses they fought against Sisera" (Judges 5:20).

Judge Gideon

God used a solar eclipse to clothe Gideon in the Holy Spirit and rallied Israel against their oppressor.

On August 19, 1157 BC, fifty years after Deborah witnessed the solar eclipse that led Israel to victory over their enemies, Gideon also witnessed a solar eclipse that would lead him to victory over the Midianites.

Historians believe Gideon lived around this time in west Manasseh. Star charts indicate that an extreme solar eclipse occurred at this time and location. Lastly, Gideon described this supernatural event in terms people of his time could understand. When all the facts are put together, one can conclude that Gideon witnessed a solar eclipse.

When Deborah's and Gideon's eclipse stories are lined up back-to-back, the biblical timeline aligns with the stars' timeline. Fifty years before Gideon, Deborah ruled as a Judge for 40 years. After Deborah died in 1147 BC, Israel began to sin. This duration is not given, but three years would be a reasonable amount of time. Once Israel's three years of sinning ended, they entered seven years of oppression in 1150 BC. After seven years of oppression, in 1157 BC, Gideon became the next judge. Seeing that the star charts match the statements of time and locations from the Bible for Deborah and Gideon's experience, the probability of this fingerprint of time belonging to Deborah and Gideon is highly probable.

Requirement Versus Self-Desire

All four of these individuals are known to be in the correct location at the correct time of a known solar eclipse. They then give descriptive language that describes a solar eclipse. With all four data points lining up, one can easily conclude they witnessed the solar eclipses. Seeing that they witnessed these events, one now has to ask whether this is enough to fulfill Scripture or demand God perform a second miracle that cannot be explained. Suppose the first miracle of the solar eclipse occurrence is more than enough to explain the Scripture. In that case, the only reason not to accept it and demand something else is purely self-desire versus a requirement.

Restoring the Ancient Israelite Calendar (Appendices A, B, and C)

Historians traditionally take best guesses as to the correct placement of events. However, the timelines they create are bound primarily to themselves, not to a concrete timeline. On the other hand, the night sky stars are part of a consistent clockwork pattern that began at creation and will persist until termination. The timeline of the stars can be calculated with precision because no man can move them. On the other hand, man can manipulate human history, and if events are not paired with a concrete timeline, the resulting dates could be off by a large sum of years.

The Bible timeline can be aligned with the star timeline by considering Israel's lunar months with correlating Passovers and sabbaths. In doing this, one can find the only date associated with the event by lining up several lunar-related sabbaths with the stars.

The astronomical calendar events that this book looked at were the Exodus day, the day when manna started to fall, the first Passover in the Promised Land, and the Jubilee cycle. When all these events are put together, the star calendar's resulting date would be the only correct calendar date for the events.

The Israelite lunar month study revealed that the only Exodus year that facilitates all the sabbaths is 1524 BC.

The Story of Abraham

On (15 Nisan), April 28, 1954 BC, precisely 430 years before the Exodus from Egypt on (15 Nisan), April 17, 1524 BC, Abraham exited the city of Ur at the age of 13 years old to go to the land of Canaan. This is Passover day 430 years before the Exodus to the exact same day, 15 Nisan, as Moses pointed out at the Exodus from Egypt.

On the night of September 14, 1884 BC, and the morning of September 15, 1884 BC, Abraham and God entered into the land promise. The covenant was for an inheritance of land that was to be given 400 years later that occurred as promised in 1484 BC. The land inheritance ceremony was binding to Abraham's yet-to-be-born children. The ceremony occurred in the Promised Land, most likely the lower part around Jerusalem and Abraham's home. Historians estimate the timing of the ceremony to this time. Abraham's description of the ceremony adheres to what an eclipse would have been. The star charts also collaborate that an extreme solar eclipse occurred over this location, matching the Bible description of the event.

Moses

Moses witnessed the burning bush total solar eclipse in 1533 BC. Then, nine years later, he leads the Exodus from Egypt. Thus, the Exodus occurred on Saturday, 15 Nisan, 1524 BC, the day after the Passover lamb was sacrificed. The Exodus from Egypt occurred exactly to the self-same day Abraham exited Ur 430 years earlier, on 15 Nisan.

Joshua

Israel entered the Promised Land in 1484 BC, 40 years after 1524 BC, precisely 400 years after the covenant between Abraham and God in 1884 BC. This resulted in the first Passover lamb being sacrificed in the Promised Land on Friday evening, 14 Nisan, 1484 BC, which was a sabbath. This entrance into the Promised Land and subsequent Passover marked the 400 years to the exact year from Abraham's covenant promise to inherit the land for his offspring.

The campaign by Israel to claim the Promised Land lasted just over seven years. The battle for Gibeon when the sun stopped, a solar eclipse, occurred on June 1, 1478 BC. This event occurred after five years of war for the Promised Land. The war ended on September 24, 1477 BC, the 10th day of the seventh month, the Day of Atonement. Caleb turned 85 years old, and the land was divided, starting the first Jubilee. This Jubilee also lines up with Jeremiah's Jubilee.

Hebrew History Covered in Light of Star Chart Dates

- Abraham was born in 1967 BC.
- Abraham exits Ur at 13 years of age on April 28, 1954 BC.
- Abraham and God enter into a land covenant on the night of Sunday, September 14 and the morning of Monday, September 15, 1884 BC.
- Isaac was born in 1867 BC.
- Jacob was born in 1807 BC.
- Joseph was born in 1716 BC.
- Joseph dies in 1606 BC.
- Moses was born in 1604 BC.
- Moses sees the burning bush on Wednesday, May 9, 1533 BC.
- Israel's Passover in Egypt occurred on Friday, April 16, 1524 BC.
- Israel's Exodus from Egypt happens on Saturday, April 17, 1524 BC.
- The first Sabbath after manna starts falling on Saturday, 21 Ziv, 1524 BC.
- The first Passover in the Promised Land on Friday evening to Saturday morning April 23, 1484 BC.
- The battle of Gibeon occurs on Tuesday, May 31, 1478 BC.
- The first Jubilee occurred on the Day of Atonement on September 24, 1477 BC.
- Judge Deborah sees the stars fighting on October 30, 1207 BC.

- Gideon was clothed by the Holy Spirit on Tuesday, August 19, 1156 BC.
- God speaks to King Solomon on Monday, January 27, 932 BC.
- King Zedekiah reigns during the 18th Jubilee which happened in 595 BC.

Probability

What are the odds of the following four events lining up on the purposed Exodus date?

1. Israel's exodus from Egypt was 15 Nissan on a Saturday.
2. Mana fell for six days, then a sabbath.
3. The first Passover in the Promised Land was on 15 Nisan, a Saturday.
4. The 18th Jubilee in 595 BC.

The odds of all four of these events lining up with the purposed Exodus day is 1/3,601 and is precisely what is seen within the Exodus date of 1524 BC.

The probability of two sunrise eclipses, one for Abraham and one for Joshua, is greater than one year out of 100 years each. The probability of both these eclipses occurring at the interval as described in the Bible is 1/10,000, indicating only one year in 10,000 years will this sequence of events occur.

The odds of a sunset eclipse occurring when Moses was in the mountains is about 1/100. The burning bush only had a 1 in 100 years possibility of occurring.

The probability of sabbaths, Passovers, Jubilees, and three solar eclipses as described is:

1/7x2/7x1/3x1/49x1/100x1/100x1/100= 1/3,601,500,000.

What does 1 year in 3 billion 600 million years mean? The significance of this is that only one year in all of the biblical times will line up with the astronomical calendar. At first glance, this may not seem like a big thing. However, once the Bible timeline is lined up against days, weeks and solar eclipses, the probability of all this occurring as it did is 1/3,601,500,000. By lining up all these events in the Bible timeline with the astronomical timeline, only one day will match, and it is the day of the Exodus from Egypt! In other words, as much as one can look through all of the biblical times, this exact sequence of events will not reoccur again! To put this into perspective, only 3,500 years have passed since the Exodus in 1524 BC to now! The only way to account for the calendar lining up against such statistically high odds is to conclude that it occurred as the Bible stated!

God has always given man a choice to follow Him or not. Israel chose to give all credit for the Exodus from Egypt to the bull god Apis. Moses chose to give God credit for the burning bush total solar eclipse. Years later, Moses again gave God credit for the Exodus from Egypt.

Just as Israel and Moses had a choice, we also choose to accept or not accept any evidence dealing with the Bible. We choose to look at the evidence and say this is proof that God loves us, or we can look at the evidence and say this is evidence that God did not do it. I hope that everyone reading this will see how God played a role in developing His people and will understand

God's love for us—a love that allows everyone to make their own decision to believe or not to believe.

APPENDICIES

A

Chronology

The Bible's chronology is more verifiable than all other historical chronologies. The Bible provides the first people's names created by God and continues a running genealogy to Jesus.

Historians, however, still disagree on some chronology durations found within the Bible. Some historians argue that years are missing, so they pack hundreds of years into the timeline when there should only be a few. Other historians claim the reported hundreds of years that the Bible gives are too much, so they crush it into a few years. This book will establish the most accurate Bible timeline possible using a Bible-first approach and then be supported by other timelines—but not changed by them.

A chronology breathes life into civilizations from long ago. These cultures, often merely mentioned, are just a group of people. However, associating a family chronology places life within that society. It is one thing to say a culture exists; it is another to give the ancestral history from its patriarch to any given point.

A perpetual chronology brings life into that ancient society. When viewed within a particular culture, this tracking of life and time gives a dimension of time to that society. This time dimension allows for stories to be told and lives to be lived. When looking at tombstones, the *dash* between the birth date and the death date represents a person's life and deeds. Establishing a chronology of key individuals—dashes, if you will, in history—can bring ancient cultures and societies back to life and learn from them.

The chronology timeline of a society allows for the establishment of a world timeline. Once the timeline of various societies has been established, they can be overlapped. If done correctly, the overlapping will all line up, giving the ability to see what happened in each civilization at any given point in time. The timelines of the civilizations grow more robust and more accurate as society timelines are combined. By finding associations within two cultures, we can bring life to both. One patriarch's association in one society to a patriarch of another society binds both society's timelines together. The linking of all societal chronologies into one world chronology allows for an overarching timeline for the world.

The timelines established through chronologies are only as accurate as of the historian's associations within the chronologies. Ancestral timelines for tribes, regional, and world chronologies are only as good as those making the connections. Several hurdles exist in linking a civilization's chronology. For instance, the languages may be different, individuals may be known by different names in each culture, and some societies have more gaps in their recorded timelines than others. These variables and more could throw off the timeline by hundreds of years.

Historians must rank each society's chronological timeline then stack them in the order of their accuracy. An example is if an Egyptian Pharaoh is proved to be the one who opposed God and Moses during the Exodus. In such a case, which method should be employed to determine the exact year in history he opposed God? The most popular option is to go to Egyptian chronology, take the date assigned to the Pharaoh, and apply it to the Exodus. Another option is to take the date assigned within the Bible to the Exodus and apply that to the Egyptian chronology.

The first method starts with a base timeline of the Egyptian culture and then adjusts the Bible to fit that timeline. The second option starts with the Bible as the baseline and adjusts the Egyptian timeline to the biblical timeline. As seen, the historian chooses which chronology to give more weight to: is it the Egyptians or the Israelites? Traditional historians use the Egyptian timeline as the base for their biblical timeline and then place the Israelite timeline on the Egyptian timeline. At first glance, this could appear logical, assuming the historian is picking the most intact and accurate timeline. However, determining which timeline is the most intact and accurate is subjective.

Most secular historians consider the Egyptian timeline to be the most detailed and complete timeline available, going back before the time of Moses. The Egyptian timeline is impressive. However, historians are not in agreement on the duration of several periods of Egyptian history. When surveying the length of time from 1500 BC to now, there is roughly a 100-year discrepancy between the historians' timelines.

Most timelines have gaps in their historical records. The primary concern with any timeline is unknown or missing lengths of time. Secular historians argue that the Bible timeline is full of gaps, making it less dependable than the Egyptian timeline. In fact, the Bible timeline is complete, surpassing the Egyptian timeline.

Historians look at significant events that transcend cultures to minimize time discrepancies, enabling timeline attachments around that event. When historians know of an event, such as a volcano eruption, they can find the impact of that event upon the various civilizations. The events allow for linking all impacted societies and thus establishing one timeline. The problem, however, is that most historical events are also open to personal opinion as to when they occurred.

Timelines based on personal opinions tend to be less accurate than those based on a mathematically provable chain of events. While combining societal timelines establishes a more reliable timeline, there is still room for opinion on connecting those timelines, introducing a significant opportunity for error. Timelines based on a mathematically provable chain of events remove personal opinion and introduce fact.

The primary method of establishing correct dates involves linking events from timelines that cannot be adjusted. One timeline that cannot be adjusted is astronomical history. Astronomical history can never be changed. Once it was set in motion, it will stay in motion. Astronomical calculations can be run forward and backward at any point in time without changing the results. The astronomical clock is the most incorruptible baseline available to us. Therefore, the Bible and astronomical charts are the most trustworthy timelines known to exist.

Over the last 200 years, astrophysicists have calculated the celestial timeline. The Holy Spirit has blessed us with a calendar in the sky that has no discrepancies. The advancement of physics over the last 200 years has led to breakthroughs in understanding how to calculate this timeline. Physicists have learned how to calculate the earth's orbit around the sun and the moon around the earth. Physicists have learned that the earth is slowing down. Astrophysicists can model what is in the sky today or 3,000 years in the future or 3,000 years in the past. The astronomical timelines can be considered scientific evidence based on our ability to accurately model any moment in time: present, future, or past.

The Bible timeline provides human history, such as genealogy and information regarding astronomical events. Ancient Israel calculated the beginning of all their months based on the lunar cycle. The astronomical timeline strengthens the biblical timeline, providing exact dates for events such as the rising moon's locations on the horizon and total solar eclipses that would have impacted Israel. The Bible timeline, when used as the baseline, can be strengthened by overlapping the astronomical timeline onto it.

One significant benefit of overlapping the Bible and astronomical timelines is that it proves the Bible is accurate!

Many Christians have used the astronomical timeline in the past for dating biblical events. Archbishop Ussher, in 1658 AD, made the most comprehensive chronological studies of his time, and within it, he used the word eclipse over 100 times. Several commentators, such as *Ellicott's Commentary on the Bible*, mention the idea of solar eclipses being described in the Bible.

Determining when and where Bible events occurred allows for an accurate timeline to be established. For the first time, calculations for days of weeks and solar eclipses can be accurately performed, and when lined up with the Bible, more accurate timelines can be established. Studying the firsthand accounts of Bible events and examining the known natural phenomenon that took place at the same time will shed light and further understanding of the Scripture.

Through a Bible-first approach with secondary inputs, this book will uncover exact biblical dates. The Bible is the primary reference for this book, and any additional input will be taken from Bible scholars, secular historians, and astronomical data. By combining all available resources, an accurate chronology of the Bible will be revealed.

Calculating Past Time

One challenge for mathematicians in calculating past time is finding the rate of the earth's rotational decay. The earth continuously slowing down from year to year, which averaged over five seconds a year over the last 2,000 years. The rotation speed decay results from many factors. Earth's slowing can come from ocean tides, volcanic eruptions, earthquakes, and meteorite impacts.

Scientists have gone through star charts and events in the sky, such as eclipses, and adjusted this decay rate to match historical records. In doing this, mathematicians can calculate formulas that model the decay rate. The formula for this is known as the *Delta-T* calculation and gives us the ability to accurately calculate the earth's rotation speed for any given time.

The determination of *Delta-T*, according to Fred Espenak and Jean Meeus stated in the NASA Scientific and Technical Information (STI) publication titled, "NASA/TP–2009– 214174," is calculated as stated: "Outside the period of observations (500 BCE to 2005 CE), the value of *Delta-T* can be extrapolated from measured values using the long-term mean parabolic trend: *Delta-T* = –20 + 32u2s, where u = (year – 1820)/100, and is defined as time measured in centuries."[53]

This book uses this *Delta-T* for finding the eclipses and the phases of the moon. The primary reason for using this *Delta-T* formula is its wide acceptance as the gold standard for astronomical charts dating back thousands of years.

NASA used this *Delta-T* to develop a list of astronomical events listed in Fred Espenak and Jean Meeus NASA Scientific and Technical Information (STI) publication titled "NASA/TP– 2009–214174."

The calculated times within the mentioned NASA publication are given as the time of the greatest eclipse covering the earth and in the form of Universal Time. This book is only concerned

---

[53] NASA, Fred Espenak and Jean Meeus, *Five Millennium Catalog of Solar Eclipses: -1999 to +3000 (2000 BC to 3000 CE) – Revised (NASA/TP-2009-214174)*, (NASA, JANUARY 2009), Page 12.

with the eclipse viewers' perspective and gives eclipse times in the viewer's local time. Using local time versus universal time and individual perspective time versus greatest eclipse time results in different times for the event and, in one case, a different day. Even though there is a variation in time and potentially day, it is the same eclipse, just in different time measurements.

B

Exodus Timeline

Israel's Exodus from Egypt is one of the best-documented events in the Bible. This chapter will evaluate the traditional Exodus dates and circumstances that would both positively and negatively impact these dates.

The 1280 BC Exodus Date

Some scholars place the Exodus around 1280 BC. The primary reason is that Israel lived in a city called Pi-Ramesses. The argument claims that the city was constructed in 1280 BC. Therefore, the Exodus from that city could not happen until after its construction.

The Bible tells us that Israel built and left from the city of Pi-Ramesses. However, it does not mean that they built and left the exact city constructed in 1280 BC. The city of Pi-Ramesses was built over the site of Avaris, a city destroyed in 1524 BC. Since both towns are located at the exact location, one could call it by either name: Pi-Ramesses or Avaris. So, depending upon what one believes about the name of the city that the

Children of Israel left will determine if they believe the event happened before or after 1280 BC.

A 1280 BC Exodus's viability can be determined by comparing it to the known date of the temple construction. First, one must subtract the proposed Exodus date, 1280 BC, from 966 BC, when temple construction started, giving the time between the events. The calculation shows that a minimum of 314 years separated the Exodus date of 1280 BC from the beginning of the temple construction. These 314 years include 40 years in the wilderness, 40 years for King Saul, 40 years for King David, and four years for the beginning of the temple's construction under King Solomon. Once the stated times are subtracted from 314 years, 190 years are left for the judges, spanning Joshua to Samuel.

Three scriptural time restraints cast uncertainty on the 1280 BC Exodus date.

The first restraint to evaluate 1280 BC against will be 1 Kings 6:1. This verse requires 480 years between the start of the temple construction and the Exodus from Egypt. Since 480 years is longer than 314 years, this creates a problem. The date 1280 BC does not account for some 166 extra years mentioned in 1 Kings 6:1.

The second restraint is mentioned in Acts 13:20, where Luke tells us that Israel was given the Judges for about 450 years. This presents the same problem since 1280 BC only allows for 190 years for the Judges. Acts 13:20 shows that the 1280 BC date is not viable.

The third restraint is mentioned in Judges 11:26, stating that some 300 years passed between the conquest of the Promised Land up to Jephthah. Since 300 years is still greater than the 190 years for the Judges, there is no way the Exodus date of 1280 BC is viable.

Three Scriptures, 1 Kings 6:1, Acts 13:20, and Judges 11:26, show no way an Exodus date of 1280 BC is viable.

The 1446 BC Exodus

Another popular way for scholars to calculate the Exodus is to focus on 1 Kings 6:1, which says, "It came to pass in the four hundred and eightieth year after the children of Israel were come out of the land of Egypt, in the fourth year of Solomon's reign over Israel, in the month Zif, which is the second month, that he began to build the house of the LORD."

Using this evidence, we can calculate the Exodus per 1 Kings 6:1. Starting with 966 BC (the date of temple construction started) and adding 480 years (the length of time from 1 Kings 6:1) this gives us 1446 BC.

The date 1446 BC is a simple conclusion but does not meet the test of continuity with other Scriptures.

The first problem with 1446 BC is that it does not allow enough time. Acts 13:20 tells us that the time of the Judges lasted 450 years. This does not include 84 years for three kings, 40 years in the wilderness, and seven years for the conquest of Canaan. According to Acts, 581 years is needed, but 1 Kings 6:1 only allows for 480 years, a deficiency of 101 years.

Two commentators Barns and Lumby express concern over the apparent conflict between Scripture.

Barn's Notes on the Whole Bible — "Though the books of Joshua, Judges, and Samuel furnish us with no exact chronology, they still supply important chronological data - data which seem to indicate for the interval between the Exodus and Solomon, a period considerably exceeding 480 years."[54]

The Pulpit Commentary — "It is difficult to reconcile this statement with other chronological notices both of the Old and New Testament. For taking the numbers which we find in the Hebrew text of the books which refer to this period, they sum up to considerably more than 480 years. The time of the Judges alone comprises 410 years at the least."[55]

The argument for the 1446 BC Exodus is based on the 480 years. However, the math shows that this date does not hold up to internal scrutiny.

Septuagint and Oppression Dates

The "480 years" comes from the Masoretic translation of the Old Testament in Hebrew. The Roman Catholic and subsequently the Protestant Bibles relied on the Masoretic text as our Old Testament source. The Masoretic translation was

---

[54] Albert Barns, *Notes on the Whole Bible.*

[55] Joseph S. Exell. *The Pulpit Commentary, I Kings (New York: Funk and Wagnalls), p. 99.*

completed around 900 AD. The Masoretic translation was translated from the Quattuordecim, which was the primary translation made by Ezra and used by Jews at the time of Jesus. Jesus and His apostles did not use the Masoretic translation that we use because it was not made until several hundred years later.

One translation error that has occurred is in 1 Kings 6:1. The Masoretic text has 480 years; however, the Septuagint has only 440 years. This 40-year difference is a reason for a pause since the Bible tells us it is exactly 480 or 440 depending on the translation. Many put total faith in a number that appears to have the potential of being 40 years off.

Adjusting the timeline to include adequate time would require more information. This is where *Cambridge Bible for Schools and Colleges* proposes a solution:

"It is most likely that the 440 years of the Septuagint (LXX) was arrived at by adding together the years assigned to the several judges and omitting the other events, the oppression of Jabin, and of the Philistines. This makes a total 296 years, which with 40 years for the sojourn in the desert, and 104 between Eli and the 4th year of Solomon brings the total to 440."[56]

The *Cambridge Bible for Schools and Colleges* has a possible solution for this verse that will put the Whole Bible in harmony. They found that when all of Israel's good years are added up in

---

[56] J. S. Perowne, *The Cambridge Bible for Schools and Colleges* (Cambridge: University Press, 1896), p. 54.

Judges, a total of 296 years is calculated. They then add 104 years for the time from Eli up to the start of the temple construction. The resulting years are 440, the same as the Septuagint. They then propose to add the years of oppression for the correct number of years.

The *Cambridge Bible* has a good observation: the judges' time period has years of oppression where no judge ruled and was not added to this number. Thus, one needs to add the years of oppression to 440 to get the correct answer.

The Cambridge Bible for Schools and Colleges does not calculate for overlapping timeframes. This method's primary concern is the years of oppression and years of the Judges running independently, back-to-back, with no overlapping. Most historians place several of these years running simultaneously, such as two Judges governing at the same time.

The primary problem with determining that there cannot be any overlap in timeframes is that the Bible does not say they did or did not. Therefore, mandating one way or the other without further Scripture would be irresponsible.

The primary reason for adding the years of oppression to the 440 or 480 years is that it lines up with the rest of the Bible. Acts 13:20 tells us that the time of the Judges lasted 450 years. To include 84 years for the kings, 40 years in the wilderness, and 7 years for the conquest of Canaan. According to Acts, 581 years is needed, but 1 Kings 6:1 allows for 480 years, a deficiency of 101 years. Furthermore, if we instead use the 440 years, we still have a deficiency of 141 years. The years discrepancy is remedied once the years of oppression are added, making the numbers closer aligned.

One possibility as to why the years of oppression could have been left off is that, 2,500 years ago, they only included the years of self-government in the national record. If someone else is governing you, how can that be your governing?

The years of oppression mentioned in Judges occurs in 6 verses: Judges 3:8, 3:14, 4:3, 6:1, 10:8, and 13:1. The time of oppression in all six verses is rounded to whole numbers and are 8, 18, 20, 7, 18, and 40. The total of years of oppression equals 111 years. Since we are dealing with whole years, it is clear that they were rounded. We do not know if they were rounded up or down.

The dilemma with rounding 6 numbers means there is up to 6 years either added or lost. One does not know if days, weeks, or months were added or subtracted. We do not know if they counted the whole year by starting a new year, even by one day. The result of uncertainty with these six numbers is that they could be just shy of 6 years off in either direction.

The 440 years or 480 years are a culmination of all Israel's events and may have been rounded. There are 13 dates given in Judges that equal 279 years; all 13 are also rounded, providing 161 or 201 years for the other Bible events. The good news is that the 440 or 480 are a complete set of years. However, they may not be whole numbers, meaning they could be off as much as one year in either direction.

Adding the 111 years of oppression mentioned in Judges to the 440 and 480 years, we get 551 and 591 years.

All the numbers in the Bible are now similar and no longer contradict each other. The 551 years or 591 years are better aligned with the Bible's genealogy and are closer to the years that Acts 13 gives us, being about 581 years. The numbers no longer contradict each other but rather strengthen each other, seeing they are about 30 years and 10 years off, depending upon which one you choose.

There is one main difference between the verse in Acts and Kings. Acts 13 dates are estimations but not exact. The number given in 1 Kings 6:1 was intended to calculate down to one sum of years.

The 581 years given to us in Acts come with the disclaimer "about." The word "about" was placed in front of all numbers given to us in Acts, implying estimates, not exact years. So they could be off by several years.

The 440 years or 480 years given in 1 Kings 6:1 calculate to an exact year. We read in 1 Kings 6:1, "It came to pass in..." This would imply an exact rounded year, not an estimation. This number would be expected to contain the correct measurement unit—in this case, the correct year. The only adjustments that need to be made are for the rounding to whole years. As a result of the numbers in 1 Kings 6:1 being more specific than Acts 13, our efforts will be concentrated around them. The final numbers for 440 and 480 with the 111 years of oppression added will be 551 years and 591 years respectively when added to 966 BC (the 4th year of King Solomon). This means the dates in question for the Exodus are 1517 BC or 1557 BC, plus or minus seven years for rounding.

Conclusion

The Exodus window's most probable dates are: 1524 – 1510 BC from the Septuagint and 1564 – 1550 BC from the Masoretic. In addition to the two sets of years, the 1280 BC and 1446 BC timeframe will also be evaluated. By evaluating these four sets of times, the hope is to encapsulate the actual Exodus date.

C

Triangulating the Exodus

Triangulation is the science of looking for one specific point by seeking multiple individual events that intersect the sought-after point.

This chapter will seek the Exodus date by looking for the intersection point of many events that the Exodus must have in common. For instance, if one knows that a Sabbath must occur on an exact day of a month, one can rule out any years that do not have a Sabbath on that specific day. After employing this method for many data points, the list of possible Exodus dates will be reduced to one viable Exodus date. The Exodus date calculation would then be calculated, not based on seeking a particular date, but rather the triangulation (intersection point) of the Exodus timeline's multiple requirements.

The Jubilee

A triangulation data point for the Exodus date is a Jubilee that occurred within King Zedekiah's reign. This section will evaluate when the Jubilee occurred and compile a list of potential Exodus years that line up with King Zedekiah's Jubilee.

The Jubilee cycle started after the division of the Promised Land to the Tribes of Israel and occurred every forty-nine years. The first Jubilee cycle started when Joshua divided the land on the Day of Atonement and then reoccurred every forty-nine years. The Jubilee starts on the tenth day of the tenth month (the Day of Atonement). The Jubilee Year, the fiftieth year, is also the first year in the next forty-nine-year cycle. Thus, the Jubilee would follow every forty-nine years, being the fiftieth year and the start of the next forty-nine-year cycle. "And ye shall hallow the fiftieth year, and proclaim liberty throughout the land unto all the inhabitants thereof: it shall be a Jubilee unto you; and ye shall return every man unto his possession, and ye shall return every man unto his family" (Leviticus 25:10). The Jubilee cycles are also referred to as the seven sets of seven years; hence seven times seven is 49 years.

The Prophet Jeremiah emphasized that King Zedekiah did not celebrate the Jubilee by using the critical language in the past tense: "Therefore thus saith Jehovah: Ye have not hearkened unto me, in proclaiming liberty, every man to his brother, and every man to his neighbor: behold, I proclaim unto you a liberty, saith Jehovah, to the sword, to the pestilence, and to the famine; and I will make you to be tossed to and fro among all the kingdoms of the earth" (Jeremiah 34:17). King Zedekiah is accused of not celebrating the Jubilee as seen in the fact that he did not proclaim liberty to the slaves. Jeremiah used the critical statement "proclaiming liberty" which is reserved for the Jubilee as Ellicott's commentary explains: "The phrase 'proclaim liberty' was closely connected with the year of

Jubilee, as in Leviticus 25:10 and Isaiah 61:1."[57] Barnes agrees: "To proclaim liberty unto them - The words are those of the proclamation of the year of Jubilee to the people, whereupon it became their duty to set their slaves free."[58] This indicates the Jubilee occurred before (Jeremiah 34:17).

King Zedekiah refused to celebrate the Jubilee before the three-year siege by the Babylonians. King Zedekiah ruled Israel for 11 years, and the last three years were under siege. The return of the Babylonians resulted in the destruction of Jerusalem. Based on that, King Zedekiah's skipping of the Jubilee had to have occurred before the return of the Babylonians: "Behold, I will command, saith Jehovah, and cause them to return to this city; and they shall fight against it, and take it, and burn it with fire: and I will make the cities of Judah a desolation, without an inhabitant" (Jeremiah 34:22). This Scripture demonstrates that the Jubilee happened within the first eight years of King Zedekiah's reign. This means that the Jubilee was between 594 and 586 BC.

The timing for the Jubilee can be narrowed down to one year. The Bible says in Jeremiah 28:1 that, "In the beginning of the reign of Zedekiah king of Judah," that Hananiah prophesied that Babylon would relinquish control over Israel, and all captives would return within two full years: "Within two full years will I bring again into this place all the vessels of Jehovah's house, that Nebuchadnezzar king of Babylon took away from this place, and carried to Babylon: and I will bring again to this

---

[57] Plumptre, Edited by Charles John Ellicott, *Commentary for English Readers, Vol. V* (New York: Cassell and Company, 1884), p. 119.

[58] Albert Barns. *Notes on the Whole Bible.*

place Jeconiah the son of Jehoiakim, king of Judah, that went to Babylon, saith Jehovah; for I will break the yoke of the king of Babylon" (Jeremiah 28:3-4). The false Prophet Hananiah used the Jubilee in King Zedekiah's second year as the end time of Israel's oppression and restoration. The Jubilee would have occurred in the second year of King Zedekiah, being 595 BC.

Hananiah was quoting Isaiah. Isaiah's book was written roughly 125 years before this event, so the book and its prophesies would be well known in Israel. Hananiah's prophesies are based on Isaiah's statements concerning the Jubilee.

Isaiah has two chapters that cover the Jubilee. The first chapter is 58 and the second is chapter 61. Chapter 58 focuses on correcting Israel's sins so they will be prepared for the Jubilee. Chapter 61 concentrates on the joys of the Jubilee. Both of these chapters cover different aspects of the Jubilee.

Jesus reads from Isaiah: "The Spirit of the Lord is upon me, because he has anointed me to preach good tidings to the poor: He has sent me to proclaim freedom to the captives, and recovering of sight to the blind, to set at liberty them that are bruised, to proclaim the acceptable year of the Lord" (Luke 4:18-19). The passage that Jesus recited from Isaiah does not exist in its stated form. The passage that Jesus read is a compilation of two verses covering the Jubilee and combined by Jesus. Jesus read (Isaiah 61:1-2) leaving out the statement "opening of the prison to them that are bound" and inserted Isaiah 58:6, more specifically, Jesus quoted the Greek Septuagint exactly from Isaiah 58:6.

The combining of two similar chapters was a common practice during the time of Jesus. It was common to take two chapters that speak of the same thing and combine them into one. This practice is not common today, but commentaries are written similarly with the primary verse first then a cluster of similar verses listed after. The primary intention of combining two like passages was to gain a fuller understanding. By combining both these chapters, Jesus confirms that both chapters 58 and 61 of Isaiah speak of the Jubilee and together make a complete picture.

Isaiah outlines the expectations of a complete restoration of Israel on the Jubilee:

Isaiah 61:1-4 – "The Spirit of the Lord Jehovah is upon me; because Jehovah hath anointed me to preach good tidings unto the meek; he hath sent me to bind up the broken-hearted, to proclaim liberty to the captives, and the opening of the prison to them that are bound; To proclaim the year of Jehovah's favor, and the day of vengeance of our God; to comfort all that mourn; To appoint unto them that mourn in Zion, to give unto them a garland for ashes, the oil of joy for mourning, the garment of praise for the spirit of heaviness; that they may be called trees of righteousness, the planting of Jehovah, that he may be glorified. And they shall build the old wastes, they shall raise up the former desolations, and they shall repair the waste cities, the desolations of many generations."

Hananiah used Isaiah's words to proclaim that God was with Israel and will restore them. However, Jeremiah proclaimed that God was not pleased with Israel.

Jeremiah 11:6-7 – "Jehovah said unto me, Proclaim all these words in the cities of Judah, and in the streets of Jerusalem, saying, Hear ye the words of this covenant, and do them. For I earnestly protested unto your fathers in the day that I brought them up out of the land of Egypt, even unto this day, rising early and protesting, saying, Obey my voice."

Hananiah's reference to the restoration of Israel, the returning of captives, and vengeance against their enemy if they remove the yoke of Jeremiah is reminiscent of the following verse:

Isaiah 58:9-10 – "Then shalt thou call, and Jehovah will answer; thou shalt cry, and he shall say, Here I am. If thou take away from the midst of thee the yoke, the putting forth of the finger, and speaking Wickedly; And if thou draw out thy soul to the hungry, and satisfy the afflicted soul; then shall thy light rise in darkness, and thine obscurity be as the noonday."

The directions in Isaiah 58 and the actions taken against Jeremiah are the same:

Jeremiah 28:10-11 – "Then Hananiah the Prophet took the yoke from off the Prophet Jeremiah's neck, and break it. And Hananiah spoke in the presence of all the people, saying, thus saith Jehovah; Even so will I break the yoke of Nebuchadnezzar king of Babylon within two full years from off the neck of all the nations. And the Prophet Jeremiah went his way."

Hananiah's breaking of the yoke of Jeremiah is reminiscent of Isaiah 58:9, which says, "Then shalt thou call, and Jehovah will answer; thou shalt cry, and he shall say, Here I am. If thou take away from the midst of thee the yoke, the putting forth of the finger, and speaking wickedly." Hananiah is twisting this verse to say that Israel is being punished because of Jeremiah. Hananiah further interprets that God would restore Israel if they pronounced Jeremiah as a false prophet. Jeremiah countered by saying God will have Babylon return and take Jerusalem: "Behold, I will command, saith Jehovah, and cause them to return to this city; and they shall fight against it, and take it, and burn it with fire: and I will make the cities of Judah a desolation without inhabitant" (Jeremiah 34:22).

It is reasonable to conclude that the event acting as the marker for Israel's restoration is a Jubilee. The Jubilee happens every 49 years, and while the 50th year is the Jubilee, it is also the start of the next set of 49 years. So the first Jubilee must be an increment of 49 years away from the Jubilee that occurred during King Zedekiah's reign.

The first-year reign of King Zedekiah was 597 BC, so It is from 597 BC that two years are added, hence 595 BC as the fulfillment of the Jubilee promise. Therefore, all the Jubilee's years can be found by starting with the year 595 BC and adding 49 years as an increment of one Jubilee. The benefit of doing this would be that the original Jubilee would fall on a descending increment of 49 years going back in time.

The years of the Jubilee are: 595, 644, 693, 742, 791, 840, 889, 938, 987, 1036, 1085, 1134, 1183, 1232, 1281, 1330, 1379, 1428, 1477, 1526, 1575, 1624 BC.

Using the Jubilee listed years then adding the years from the Exodus to the first Jubilee, the acceptable Exodus dates can be found. The first Jubilee occurred on the Day of Atonement when the land was divided at Caleb's 85th birthday; this means that the date of the very first Jubilee would be 47 years after the Exodus: 642, 691, 740, 789, 838, 887, 936, 985, 1034, 1083, 1132, 1181, 1230, 1279, 1328, 1377, 1426, 1475, 1524, 1573, 1622, 1671 BC.

The stated dates would allow the first Jubilee to occur in an interval to that of the Jubilee celebrated in King Zedekiah's reign. The odds of any year being one of these years is 1/49.

Three Sabbaths

Astronomical mathematics allows us to determine the beginning of Israel's months and subsequent days of the week. Ancient Israel does not have a set calendar; instead, it is a floating calendar dependent on the first moon's sighting. Ancient Israel starts their months at the first sighting of the new moon at sunset. To establish this beginning of the month, one would have to witness the moon's first appearance. Seeing the month's start is established only at the new moon's sighting, it is impossible to establish their ancient calendar. Thanks to astronomical mathematics, one can calculate the day Israel would have seen the new moon and subsequently establish their long-lost calendar.

One specific way this method was used is for the calculation of the date of Jesus' death. The Bible informs us Jesus died on a Friday, so mathematicians calculated Israel's calendar for that specific year. Mathematicians were able to calculate this one event because they were looking at a narrow timeframe: one month for a year for a span of no more than a few years. While this was feasible for people with slide rulers a hundred years ago, it was unfeasible to expect them to calculate every single month for every single year for thousands of years. Over time, this information sat idle and forgotten.

There was no feasible way to verify when the moon would have been spotted, so there was no reliable way to set the beginning of their months and subsequent days of weeks. However, thanks to the knowledge of astronomy and highly accurate mathematical computations in correlation with tremendous computer computing power, one can calculate every single beginning of the month for Israel. The impact is that when the Bible said the fifteenth of Nisan was a Sabbath, there is now a way to verify it. Now these Old Testament statements can be looked at and considered to be timelines of Scripture.

The Bible describes three different Sabbaths that occurred:

1. Israel's first Passover lambs were sacrificed in the Promised Land on a Sabbath Saturday at twilight.

2. After the manna started falling, Israel's first morning Sabbath was on the seventh morning after it was promised.

3. Israel's Exodus from Egypt fell on a Saturday morning.

The correct Exodus date would allow for these three Sabbaths to occur correctly on Saturday. The Exodus has a fingerprint in the Bible with its unique description, allowing for its identification. The eyewitnesses recorded several Sabbaths with exact lengths of time from the Exodus. The observations will only line up if the correct Exodus date is selected. If the wrong Exodus date is selected, the Sabbaths will not line up. This is because the Sabbaths did not occur on the same days of the month every year but changed based on a sequential pattern of seven days. The three Sabbaths probabilities combine to a 1/73 chance. Furthermore, when the Sabbaths are paired with the Jubilee, the odds fall to 1 out of 3,601. The odds of the three Sabbaths and the Jubilee lining up is only one year in 3,601 years. Finding the one year that enables the Sabbaths and Jubilee to line up would provide substantial evidence for that Exodus year.

The Promised Land Passover Sabbath

The first Sabbath in the Promised Land can be calculated by finding the first Passover in the Promised Land. Joshua informs us that the first Passover Sabbath happened on the 14th day of the first month, being 14 Nisan, after 40 years in the wilderness. Then on the following morning, Israel ate the new grain. The fact that the new grain was eaten indicates that the Omer Offering occurred after the Passover and Sabbath:

Joshua 5:10-11 – "And the children of Israel encamped in Gilgal; and they kept the Passover on the fourteenth day of the month at even in the plains of Jericho. And they did eat of the produce of the land on the morrow after the Passover, unleavened cakes, and parched grain in the selfsame day."

To determine if the Passover was on a Sabbath, one needs to look at the Omer Offering rules:

> **Leviticus 23:10-11** – "When ye are come into the land which I give unto you, and shall reap the harvest thereof, then ye shall bring the sheaf of the first-fruits of your harvest unto the priest: And he shall wave the sheaf before Jehovah, to be accepted for you: on the morrow after the Sabbath the priest shall wave it."

The Pharisees believed that the Sabbath in verse 11 automatically applied to the first day of unleavened bread when the Omer Offering occurs. The Pharisees held that the Passover was considered a Sabbath and highlighted by Hebrew Strong word 7677 and so claim the Omer Offering can be made the day immediately after Passover.

The Sadducees held that the Sabbath marks the day before the Omer Offering. They maintain, the Omer Offering can only be given on the morrow after the seventh day of the week.

What is certain is the word Sabbath used in Leviticus and Joshua is the word Sabbath (Strong's number 7676).[59] It is used only for the seventh day of the week. The word Sabbath is often interpreted as rest. Strong's word 7677[60] is used to describe a high holy day but is different from that of a Sabbath. The word Sabbath (7677) does not appear in the Joshua or Leviticus account regarding the Omer Offering. Instead, only the Sabbath

[59] James Strong, *Dictionaries of the Hebrew and Greek Words* (New York: Eaton & Mains, 1890), p. 114.

[60] Ibid, p. 114.

(7676) or the seventh day is used. In the Leviticus and Joshua account, the Omer Offering must occur on the day after the Sabbath (7676), which is Sunday morning.

The most conservative read of Joshua 5:11 is that the Sabbath (7676) is a Friday night through Saturday.

Edersheim states:

For, the Sadducees, when in office, always conformed to the prevailing Pharisaic practices.

Thus the Sadducees would have interpreted Lev. xxiii. 11, 15, 16, as meaning that the wave-sheaf (or, rather, the Omer) was to be offered on 'the morrow after the weekly Sabbath' – that is, on the Sunday in Easter week.[61]

The Sadducees that held the strictest read of the Mosaic Law are described by James Hastings, D.D., in his *Dictionary of the Bible*:

SADDUCEES—Probably the name 'Sadducee' is derived from the name Zadok, a notable priest in the time of David and Solomon (2 S 8:17, 15:24, 1 K 1:34). His descendants long played the leading part among the

---

[61] Alfred Edersheim, *The Life and Times of Jesus the Messiah, Vol. I* (New York: E. R. Herrick, 1920), p. 320.

priests, so that Ezekiel regarded them as the only legitimate priests (Ezk 40:46, 43:19, 44:15 48:11).[62]

Hastings also covers the fact that the Sadducees were in charge of everything in Jerusalem, including the high priesthood, which would include temple activities:

> In our Lord's time many of the poor priests were Pharisees. But the higher priestly families and the priests as a body were Sadducees. With them were joined the majority of the aristocratic lay families of Judea and Jerusalem. This fact gives us the key to their career. It is wrapped up in the history of the high priesthood. For two centuries after the exile the high priesthood earned the right to the leadership of the Jewish nation.[63]

It would make sense that the high priest's sect during the first Temple period would become the high priest during the second Temple period. Likewise, it would make sense that the priests, the Sadducees that took over the high priest activities for the second Temple period, would follow in the beliefs and traditions of those in the first Temple period. Nevertheless, even if this is not the case, the Sadducees were the prominent religious leaders during the entire second Temple timeframe.

Throughout the entire time that the Sadducees lead in Jerusalem, they were known for taking a conservative view and

---

[62] James Hastings, *Dictionary of the Bible* (New York: Charles Scribner's Sons, 1909), p. 818.

[63] Ibid, p. 818.

only followed the first five books of the Old Testament, the books that Moses wrote. All sacrifices and offerings would have taken place under the supervision of a high priest who was of the Sadducees.

Offerings and sacrifices would have been done according to the Mosaic Law and carried out to the Sadducees' specifications. The Sadducees' interpretation would be meaningful, seeing that they controlled all Temple sacrifices during the second and most likely first temple timeframes. The Sadducees would have only offered the Wave Offering of the Omer Offering on the first day after the Sabbath and after the Passover. This would have been the only acceptable option during the time of Jesus. Therefore, one can conclude that it was probably the acceptable way of doing things long before Jesus' time as they were descendants of Zadok the high priest.

Suppose the Sadducees had it right in the most conservative read of Moses' books. In that case, one is looking for a Sabbath Passover with the Omer Offering on Sunday morning, the day after the Sabbath and after the first Passover in the Promised Land.

The Omer Offering on Sunday morning, 15 Nisan, would also allow for the events leading up to this. Joshua 3:1-5:11 records the crossing of the Jordan River and the events associated with it. In the account of the crossing of the Jordan, a complex chain of events is recorded.

The order of events would be as follows:

- On Thursday, 5 Nisan, Israel camped at the Jordan for three days (Joshua 3:1-2). This would mean Israel arrived at the Jordan one day before the Sabbath.

- On Monday, 9 Nisan, Israel was informed they would be crossing the Jordan the next day (Joshua 3:5).

- On Tuesday, 10 Nisan, Israel crossed the Jordan (Joshua 4:19), and the males of Israel were circumcised (Joshua 5:2-8).

- After three days of healing and before twilight on the Sabbath, Saturday, 14 Nisan, the Passover Lamb was sacrificed and the Passover was eaten on Saturday night.

- The uneaten part of the lamb was burned on the morning of Sunday, 15 Nisan.

- On the same Sunday morning, the Omer Offering was made.

The placement of the Omer Offering on Sunday morning would allow for the chain of events. The odds of lining up to any year is 1 out of 7. That is, for every seven years, one year would line up with this account.

Finding the First Sabbath

Israel's first Sabbath is marked by the end of the first week of manna. God gave Israel manna for six mornings, and on the seventh morning, being the Sabbath, the manna was not sent. Two key date references will allow us to identify the date of the first Sabbath.

The first key date is the day that manna was promised:

Exodus 16:1 – Israel came unto the wilderness of Sin, which is between Elim and Sinai, on the fifteenth day of the second month after their departing out of the land of Egypt.

The second date is how long the manna fell:

Exodus 16:26 – Six days ye shall gather it; but on the seventh day is the Sabbath, in it there shall be none.

The verses tell us that on 15 Ziv, manna was promised to Israel. The manna fell for six mornings, and on the seventh morning, being the Sabbath, no manna fell.

The main difficulty with following the timeframes is that we try to apply our definition of "day" to ancient Israel's. Today, we start and end the day when we are sleeping. From the time we wake up to the time we go to sleep, it is the same day. Israel ended and began its day when they are awake. Israel's days ended at sunset at twilight, and the new day began just after sunset. The result of starting a new day at different hours causes confusion. One example is that we do not know if the manna was promised in the evening or the morning or if it first fell on the morning of 15 Ziv or 16 Ziv.

The most natural way for us to read the statement would be that God promised manna on the 15 Ziv, and it began to fall on the 16 Ziv. However, we must remember that the day began and ended differently for Israel than for us. Israel's day began at sunset and ended at sunset; if the manna was promised on the fifteenth, then the promise was made anywhere from Friday night to Saturday evening before sunset. If true, then Israel would have received the first manna on Sunday morning.

The second way to look at this would be that manna was promised on Saturday evening, 15 Ziv, then on the morning of Sunday, 15 Ziv, the first manna began to fall.

The manna fell for six mornings in a row, but on the seventh morning, no manna would fall. The 7th day would be a Sabbath, hence Saturday morning. This means that Friday morning would be the sixth morning in a row.

Two templates can be compiled from these criteria:

Template One:

1. Manna was promised on 15 Ziv either on Friday evening or Saturday morning.
2. The manna fell on the mornings of Sunday, 16 Ziv, Monday, 17 Ziv, Tuesday, 18 Ziv, Wednesday, 19 Ziv, Thursday, 20 Ziv, and Friday, 21 Ziv, but on Saturday, 22 Ziv, manna did not fall.

Template Two:

1. Manna was promised on Saturday, 15 Ziv, after sunset.
2. The manna fell on the mornings of Sunday 15 Ziv, Monday 16 Ziv, Tuesday, 17 Ziv, Wednesday, 18 Ziv, Thursday, 19 Ziv, and Friday, 20 Ziv, but on Saturday, 21 Ziv, manna did not fall.

These days of week templates can be used to compare proposed Exodus dates, and the correct one will line up with one of the two proposed templates. If it does not line up, it is not the correct Exodus date.

The first method has Friday evening and a Saturday morning as the time when manna was promised. The first manna would then fall the next morning on Sunday, 16 Ziv.

The second method would involve the promise in the evening and the manna in the morning happening on the same day, 15 Ziv. Occurring after twilight on the fifteenth day of the second month, Moses promised Israel that God would provide them food. It is worth noting that this method of calculating the first Sabbath is embraced by Josephus, the historian from Jesus' time. Josephus gives us his belief in the timing of the events in question:

So Moses placed himself in the midst of them, and told them he came to bring them from God a deliverance from their present distresses. Accordingly a little after came a vast number of quails, which is a bird more plentiful in this Arabian Gulf than anywhere else, flying over the sea, and hovered over them, till wearied with their laborious flight, and, indeed, as usual, flying very near to the earth, they fell down upon the Hebrews, who caught them, and satisfied their hunger with them, and supposed that this was the method whereby God meant to supply them with food. Upon which Moses returned thanks to God for affording them his assistance so suddenly, and sooner than he had promised them.

But presently after this first supply of food, he sent them a second; for as Moses was lifting up his hands in prayer, a dew fell down; and Moses, when he found it stick to his hands, supposed this was also come for food from God to them: he tasted it; and perceiving that the people knew not what it was, and thought it snowed, and that it was what usually fell at that time of the year, he informed them that this dew did not fall from heaven after the manner they imagined, but came for their preservation and sustenance. So he tasted it, and gave them some of it, that they might be satisfied about what he told them. They also imitated their conductor, and were pleased with the food, for it was like honey in sweetness and pleasant taste, but like in its body to bdellium, one of the sweet spices, and in bigness equal to coriander seed. And very earnest they were in gathering it; but they were enjoined to gather it equally; the measure of an omer for each one every day, because this food should not come in too small a quantity, lest the weaker might not be able to get their share, by reason of the overbearing of the strong in collecting it. However, these strong men, when they had gathered more than the measure appointed for them, had no more than others, but only tired themselves more in gathering it, for they found no more than an omer a-piece; and the advantage they got by what was superfluous was none at all, it corrupting, both by the worms breeding in it, and by its bitterness. So divine and wonderful a food was this! It also supplied the want of other sorts of food to those that fed on it; and even now, in all that place, this manna comes down in rain, according to what Moses then obtained of God, to send it to the people for their sustenance. Now the Hebrews call this food manna; for the particle man, in our language, is the asking of a question. What is this? So the Hebrews were very joyful at what was sent them from heaven. Now they made use of this food for forty years, or as long as they were in the wilderness.[64]

Josephus believed it was in the evening when the tribe of Israel approached Moses, and God provided an immediate response. Josephus believed that quail fell from the sky immediately that evening, followed by manna appearing immediately the same evening after the quail. While the Bible does not highlight the timeframe for these events, this representation could have happened.

Moses approached Israel on 15 Ziv; what is unknown is if this was a Saturday daytime or a Saturday evening event. Seeing that Saturday daytime is a different Jewish day from Saturday evening, both options must be taken as possible candidates to be sure to encompass the correct date for the first Sabbath.

The odds of either of the two templets lining up to any year are 2 out of 7—since every seven years, two years would line up with this account.

Israel Exited Egypt on a Saturday Morning

The day of the week for the Exodus can be narrowed down by considering the research for finding the first Sabbath after the

---

[64] Josephus, Translated by Whiston, *The Works of Flavius Josephus: Antiquities of the Jews* (London: John Bumpus, 1828), 3.1.5-6, p. 81.

manna started. The first Sabbath after manna started falling was on the 21 or 22 day of the second month of the Hebrew year called Ziv. The Passover occurs on the evening of the fourteenth day of the first month of the Hebrew calendar called Nisan. The only thing not known is if there were 29 days or 30 days in the month of Nisan, the year that Israel exited Egypt. Considering these facts, two variables for the month of Nisan and two variables for Ziv appear. By calculating all possible combinations of these four variables, there are four different possible calendar templates from the first Passover to the first Sabbath. The four different calendar templates calculate only three different days of the week for the Exodus.

If one calculates the first Sabbath after the manna fell to be 22 Ziv, they will subtract 29 days from that—or 30 days if the month was longer. When calculating only 29 days for the month of Nisan, the Passover occurred on Thursday evening and the Exodus on a Friday morning. If 30 days, then the Passover happened on a Wednesday night with the Exodus happening on a Thursday morning.

If one calculates the first Sabbath after the manna started to be 21 Ziv, then 29 days means the Passover happened on a Friday night and the Exodus on a Saturday morning. If 30 days, then the Passover would have happened on Thursday night and the Exodus on Friday morning.

By considering the first Sabbath after the manna began to fall, the days of the week the Exodus occurred can be narrowed down to three potential days: Thursday, Friday, or Saturday.

These possibilities can be further narrowed down to one single day. The Bible does not relate Thursday or Friday to Israel's

Exodus from Egypt. However, the Bible links the Exodus from Egypt to Saturday, the Sabbath. The Bible informs us that Israel, the people that God sanctified, is interlinked with Saturday, which God sanctified.

God sanctified two crucial things in the Old Testament. The word "sanctified" means to set aside. God set aside both the last day of creation (Genesis 2:3) and the tribe of Israel (Exodus 20:8). The use of the word "sanctified" was used for both the creation on the seventh day and for all of Israel.

Both the sanctified day and sanctified people are combined in the remembrance of the Exodus from Egypt:

Exodus 31:12-17 – And Jehovah spoke unto Moses, saying, Speak thou also unto the children of Israel, saying, Verily ye shall keep my Sabbaths: for it is a sign between me and you throughout your generations; that ye may know that I am Jehovah who sanctifieth you. Ye shall keep the Sabbath therefore; for it is holy unto you: every one that profaneth it shall surely be put to death; for whosoever doeth any work therein, that soul shall be cut off from among his people. Six days shall work be done; but on the seventh day is a Sabbath of solemn rest, holy to Jehovah; whosoever doeth any work on the Sabbath day, he shall surely be put to death. Wherefore the children of Israel shall keep the Sabbath, to observe the Sabbath throughout their generations, for a perpetual covenant. It is a sign between me and the children of Israel for ever: for in six days Jehovah made heaven and earth, and on the seventh day he rested, and was refreshed.

Deuteronomy 5:12-15 – Observe the Sabbath day, to keep it holy, as Jehovah thy God commanded thee. Six days thou shalt labor, and do all thy work; but the seventh day is the Sabbath unto Jehovah thy God: in it thou shalt not do any work, thou, nor thy son, nor thy daughter, nor thy man-servant, nor thy maid-servant, nor thine ox, nor thine ass, nor any of thy cattle, nor thy stranger that is within thy gates; that thy man-servant and thy maid-servant may rest as well as thou. And thou shalt remember that thou was a servant in the land of Egypt, and Jehovah thy God brought thee out thence by a mighty hand and by a stretched out arm: therefore Jehovah thy God commanded thee to keep the Sabbath day.

Why would God command Israel to remember their slavery in Egypt on a different day of the week other than the day they exited Egypt? The fact that both the sanctified day and the people are intertwined down to the same day gives credibility to the fact that both events occurred on the same day of the week.

Deuteronomy 5:15 – Remember that thou was a servant in the land of Egypt, and Jehovah thy God brought thee out thence by a mighty hand and by a stretched out arm: therefore Jehovah thy God commanded thee to keep the Sabbath day.

The fact that Israel, the Exodus, and the Sabbath are intertwined so much that they cannot be separated would indicate a high probability that the Exodus took place on a Saturday. The odds of the calendar allowing for a Saturday morning Exodus is 1 in 7—that is, for every seven years, one year would line up with this account. If calculated in conjunction with the first Sabbath after the manna started, the odds are 1 in 3.

The Triangulation for the Exodus

Identifying the Exodus date can now be found by identifying the date with the most data point intersections. These four independent requirements will reveal the biblical Exodus date by lining up the Jubilee requirement and the three Sabbaths.

Previously, in the Exodus Timeline,[65] two clusters of dates and two standalone dates were identified to contain the Exodus year. The years in question are 1564 – 1550 BC, 1524 – 1510 BC, 1280 BC, and 1446 BC.

The first triangulation point that will be deployed is the Jubilee year requirement. The only Exodus years that will work with the Jubilee year requirement are 642, 691, 740, 789, 838, 887, 936, 985, 1034, 1083, 1132, 1181, 1230, 1279, 1328, 1377, 1426, 1475, 1524, 1573, 1622, and 1671 BC.

- 1564 – 1550 BC – this window of time has no Jubilees that line up with these Exodus dates.
- 1446 BC – has no Jubilees around this purposed Exodus date.
- 1280 BC – has one Exodus date of 1279 BC that lines up with a Jubilee.

---

[65] Jeffrey Grimm, *Solar Eclipses in the Bible* (United States: Jeffrey Grimm 2021), appendix A.

- 1524-1510 BC – has one Exodus date of 1524 BC that allows for a Jubilee date.

The only Exodus dates that pass the first triangulation data point are 1279 BC and 1524 BC.

The first possible Exodus date based on the Jubilee triangulation is 1279 BC:

1. The first Passover in the Promised Land has the lamb sacrificed on Saturday at twilight, but this year the Passover lamb would have been sacrificed on Thursday, April 16, 1279 BC.

2. The first Sabbath after manna fell needs to be on 21 or 22 Ziv; however, on this year, Tuesday, 21 Ziv, and Wednesday, 22 Ziv, are neither a Sabbath Saturday.

3. If 1279 BC were correct, then the Exodus would be on Tuesday, April 8, 1279 BC and is not a Sabbath.

Since the Jubilee triangulation point lines up, the odds of this event occurring is 1/49; this means that for every 49 years, this combination will occur once.

The second possible Exodus date based on the Jubilee triangulation is 1524 BC.

1. Precisely 40 years after the Exodus, Israel entered the Promised Land and had their Passover. With a 1524 BC Exodus, the first Passover in the Promised Land would have occurred on Friday to Saturday, April 23, 1484 BC. This would be in keeping with a conservative read of the Mosaic Law regarding the Omer Offering on the morning after the Passover.

2. The promise of manna would have occurred on Saturday, 15 Ziv, after sunset. The manna would have fallen on the mornings of Sunday, 15 Ziv, Monday, 16 Ziv, Tuesday, 17 Ziv, Wednesday, 18 Ziv, Thursday, 19 Ziv, and Friday, 20 Ziv, but not on Saturday, 21 Ziv. The 1524 BC template shows that the events unfolded swiftly with no delay, matching the story from Josephus. God made the promise in the evening and sent it in the morning.

3. The evening before the Exodus from Egypt is known as the first Passover. This date was on Friday, April 16, 1524. The Exodus from Egypt would then have occurred on Saturday, April 17, 1524 BC.

4. The Exodus date of 1524 BC would allow for the first Jubilee to occur in 1477 BC, and on the second year of King Zedekiah's reign, the 18th Jubilee would have occurred.

The Exodus year of 1524 BC is within the most reliable window of time provided by the Bible (1524 BC to 1510 BC).

An Exodus day of Saturday, April 17, 1524 BC, allows the Jubilee and all three Sabbaths to occur on the proper days. The probability of all the triangulation datapoints lining up is 1/49x1/7x2/7x1/3, equaling 1 in 3,601. This means that one year in every 3,601 years will line up with the Exodus requirements. Considering that 1524 BC was about 3,524 years ago there would only be one year from Moses to today that would fit all the requirements.

D

Abraham's Timeline

This appendix will evaluate Scripture to establish a timeline for when Abraham lived in Canaan. Establishing the years of Abraham will first require us to establish an accurate timeline from Moses to Abraham.

How Long Did Israel Live in Egypt?

The length of time that Israel spent in Egypt is unknown. The Bible does not give us an exact number of years that Israel lived in Egypt. However, three popular views address this unknown length of years. The first popular view uses genealogy to place Israel in Egypt for about 200 years. The other views use 430 and 400 years as set lengths of times. The 430 years and 400 years will be studied later in this appendix.

Genealogy gives us insight into the time Israel lived in Egypt. The Bible names two individuals that lived in Egypt. The two individuals are Joseph and Moses. The Bible gives us exactly how long both these individuals lived. Joseph's lifespan is covered in two verses. Genesis 37:1 tells us that Joseph was about 17 years old when he was sold into slavery. The second verse of Genesis 50:22 informs us that Joseph was 110 years old when he died. By subtracting 17 from 110 years, Joseph lived in Egypt for 93 years. The second individual is found in Exodus 7:7. Moses was 80 years old at the time of the Exodus. These two numbers, 93 and 80, are the only known lengths of time that happened sequentially but simultaneously with Israel's stay in Egypt.

The only time missing is that from the death of Joseph to the birth of Moses. After Joseph died, a new king that did not know Joseph ruled over Egypt. While there could have been several Pharaohs before this new Pharaoh, the Bible does not say this was the case. Adding more Pharaohs into the timeline would be based more on emotion than facts. The Bible informs us that when the Pharaoh that knew Joseph passed away, a new one arose. The new Pharaoh made a decree that every Israelite newborn male must be cast into the river. The decree marks Moses' birth, as we are told Moses was floated down the river at that time. Then, 80 years after Moses was born, Moses led Israel out of Egypt. The 93 years of Joseph and 80 years of Moses add up to 173 years.

Joseph's death to Moses' birth is the key to determining Israel's total time in Egypt. If only one Pharaoh came to power, then the lapse in time could be as little as two years. If many generations of Pharaohs passed, then up to 257 years could have passed.

The primary motivation for 257 years to be added between Joseph and Moses is to make Israel's time in Egypt 430 years in order to match Exodus 12:40, which says, "Now the time that the children of Israel dwelt in Egypt was four hundred and thirty years. And it came to pass at the end of four hundred and thirty years." Reading this verse leaves us with the impression that Israel was in Egypt for 430 years.

The statement "in Egypt 430 years" comes from the Masoretic translation of the Old Testament that the early church did not use. The Roman Catholic and subsequently the Protestant Bibles relied on the Masoretic text as our Old Testament source. The Masoretic translation was compiled between AD 200 and AD 900. The Masoretic translation was translated from the Quattuordecim, Ezra's direct translation used by both the Jews and the early church. Jesus and His apostles did not use the Masoretic translation, because it was not made until several hundred years later.

A second Bible translation of the Old Testament is the Septuagint. The Septuagint is based on the Greek translation made from the Quattuordecim. The Septuagint is a Greek translation of the old Hebrew Quattuordecim. The Septuagint is over 200 years older than Jesus and His apostles, making this the oldest translation of the Hebrew text known to exist. The Septuagint was the direct translation of the Old Testament for the early Christians and apostles and predated the completed Masoretic by about 1,000 years.

The Masoretic and Septuagint are both translations of the Quattuordecim. This is similar to the comparison between the King James and the American Standard Version, both being translated from the Masoretic Hebrew, and they both have translation errors. The same goes for the Masoretic and Septuagint; they are both translated from the Quattuordecim, and they both may have translation errors.

Richard Ottley, in *A Handbook to the Septuagint*, states this about the Septuagint:

The oldest translation of the Hebrew Scriptures; older than the New Testament, and written in the same language. Very naturally, therefore, the Old and New Testament in Greek came together to form the Bible of the early Christian church. For five centuries or so this version of the Old Testament was dominant; translations into other languages were, as a rule, made from it, and not from the Hebrew, until the Vulgate appeared.[66]

The early Christians predominantly used the Septuagint as it was the dominant language at the time. No early Christians used the Masoretic, since it was not even translated 200 to 900 years after Jesus. The Hebrew Masoretic and Greek Septuagint translations are both translated from the Quattuordecim, and they both may have translation errors.

The Septuagint for Exodus 12:40 states, "The sojourning of the children of Israel, while they sojourned in the land of Egypt and the land of Canaan, was 430 years."

The Septuagint combines the years Israel spent in Canaan and Egypt. To this same effect, Josephus said, "They left Egypt in the month Xanthicus, on the fifteenth day of the lunar month; four hundred and thirty years after our forefather Abraham

---

[66] Richard R. Ottley, *A Handbook to the Septuagint* (London: Methuen, 1920), p. VII.

came into Canaan, but two hundred and fifteen years only after Jacob removed into Egypt."[67]

Both the Septuagint and Josephus tell us the 430 years were not just in Egypt but a combination of time spent in both Canaan and Egypt.

Comparing the 430 years to the genealogy of Moses will give us further clarity. Moses' genealogy consists of Israel's genealogy and a portion about Moses' immediate family. Moses wrote Israel's genealogy, and his personal family's genealogy then made the statement of the 430 years. Since Moses wrote his genealogy and the 430 years statement, they should fit together without contradiction.

To assist with evaluating whether or not the 430 years in Egypt is possible, let us evaluate Moses' family tree from the time Israel was in Egypt. The best start date for Joseph is when he was sold into slavery. Starting with Joseph's arrival, let us then add on every individual's entire life (birth to death) from Moses' family line that lived in Egypt. The whole years from birth to death will be used because the Bible does not provide the father's age when each son was born. This will give the maximum amount of time that will encapsulate the actual total years in Egypt.

The first step is to calculate the time that Joseph spent in Egypt alone.

---

[67] Josephus, Translated by Whiston, *The Works of Flavius Josephus: Antiquities of the Jews* (London: John Bumpus, 1828), 2.15.2, p. 75.

Genesis 37:2 tells us that Joseph was sold into slavery at 17 years of age. Genesis 42:46 informs us that Joseph was 30 years old at the start of seven years of plenty prophesied in a dream to Pharaoh (Genesis 41:53). The seven years of famine begin in Genesis 41:54. Thus Joseph lived 27 years in Egypt before his family came. We will add this number to the years that encompass Moses' family tree since the move to Egypt by Israel. This is done with an emphasis on finding the maximum amount of time possible that Israel might have been in Egypt.

Now, let us focus on Moses' timeline.

The Bible does not indicate what age Kohath (son of Levi, son of Israel) was when he came to Egypt. To error on the side of caution, we will use his entire lifespan of 133 years as if he was born during the move to Egypt (Exodus 6:18). Kohath had a son named Amram who lived 137 years (Genesis 6:20). Amram had a son named Moses (Exodus 6:20). If one supposed that both Amram and Moses were born in the same year that their fathers died, one could add up all the years of all their lives to find the maximum amount of time they spent in Egypt. Doing this gives only (133+137) 270 years. Adding Moses' time of 80 years when Israel left Egypt (Exodus 7:7) gives us (270+80) 350 years. Finally, adding Joseph's time in Egypt to Moses' family line gives us a maximum number of years of (27+350) 377 from Joseph to Moses. The total years that Israel could have been in Egypt is 377 years max.

The 377 years is less than the 430 years by 53 years—and that is assuming the greatest possible years between the genealogies possible, which is clearly overstated. This means it is physically impossible for Israel to have been in Egypt for 430 years.

The 430 Years

Moses gives us the first important date. Moses had an observance of the 430th anniversary of Israel's sojourning at the time of the Exodus from Egypt. Israel's sojourning began when Abraham left his land in Ur and went into the land of Canaan: "Now the time that the children of Israel dwelt in Egypt was four hundred and thirty years. And it came to pass at the end of four hundred and thirty years, even the selfsame day it came to pass, that all the hosts of Jehovah went out from the land of Egypt." (Exodus 12:40-41). It is important to note that according to Moses, the Exodus from Egypt was on the 430 years commemoration of the sojourning of Israel.

The 430 years started with Abraham leaving Ur and ends when Moses made the Exodus statement. To gain further understanding, let us take a look at the moment the 430 years begins: "They went forth with them from Ur of the Chaldees, to go into the land of Canaan; and they came unto Haran, and dwelt there" (Genesis 11:31). Abraham chose to go with his father out of Ur and into the land of Canaan. Abraham did not need to do this as seen in Genesis 11:27. His brother Nahor did not go with him, so one can discern that Abraham had a choice. God called Abraham out of Ur in Genesis 15:7, saying, "I am Jehovah that brought thee out of Ur of the Chaldees, to give thee this land to inherit it." Abraham listened to God and did as God asked by leaving Ur. From the moment Abraham left his home in Ur, he became a sojourner, and his descendants remained so, as Moses pointed out, 430 years later at the time of Exodus from Egypt.

214

Moses' statement compares Abraham's Exodus of Ur to Israel's Exodus from Egypt. Moses states that 430 years earlier, on the very same day, 15 Nisan, Abraham left his home in Ur. The fact that Abraham started his sojourn on the same day 430 years earlier, just as Israel was leaving Egypt, would be a uniting factor. Abraham left Ur in order to seek out God. Israel also left the sinful country of Egypt seeking God. Moses is comparing Abraham to Israel in a fashion that would empower them to unify around a form of a rallying call.

430 years of Galatians and Genesis

The New Testament also mentions 430 years:

Galatians 3:16-17 – "Now to Abraham were the promises spoken... A covenant confirmed beforehand by God, the law, which came 430 years after."

The 430 years here is referring to the Ten Commandments as the end of the 430 years. The Ten Commandments are the Jewish Law given to Moses in the same year that Israel exited Egypt. Galatians uses Moses' statement of 430 years and applies it to receiving the Ten Commandments instead of the Exodus from Egypt. Since the Exodus and the Ten Commandments occurred in the same year, there is no change in the 430 years given in the Old and New Testaments.

The 400 Years Covenant

The 400-year covenant between Abraham and God is outlined in Genesis:

Genesis 15:12-16 – "And when the sun was going down, a deep sleep fell upon Abram; and, lo, a horror of great darkness fell upon him. And he said unto Abram, know of a surety that thy seed shall be sojourners in a land that is not theirs, and shall serve them; and they shall afflict them four hundred years; And also that nation, whom they shall serve, will I judge: and afterward shall they come out with great substance. But thou shalt go to thy fathers in peace; thou shalt be buried in a good old age. And in the fourth generation they shall come hither again: for the iniquity of the Amorites is not yet full."

The verses above are a detailed breakdown of the covenant between Abraham and God. The covenant outlines that Abraham would have a child who would become a great nation and wander for 400 years—both in Egypt and Canaan. The statement, "be sojourners in a land that is not theirs, and shall serve them; and they shall afflict them four hundred years," applies to the time in both Egypt and Canaan. By applying the 400 years to the time spent in Egypt and Canaan, the timeframe would not end with the Exodus from Egypt but with the receiving of the first land promised by God. The statement, "in the fourth generation they shall come hither again," implies that Israel would reside in the Promised Land in 400 years as stated in Genesis 15:7, which says, "I am Jehovah that brought thee out of Ur of the Chaldees, to give thee this land to inherit it."

God gave Abraham a timetable of 400 years, covering four generations. The interaction between God and Abraham included details that Abraham could not have understood, so God summarized His promises in terminology that Abraham would understand:

Genesis 15:18 – "In that day Jehovah made a covenant with Abram, saying, unto thy seed have I given this land, from the river of Egypt unto the great river, the river Euphrates."

The covenant made between Abraham and God gave his descendants the land of Canaan, a land currently possessed by the Amorites. Regardless, this fulfillment would not occur until after 400 years.

The covenant was reinforced in Genesis 26:3-4 and again in Genesis 28:13-14. This covenant is echoed by Moses to Israel while in the wilderness, indicating that it had not yet been fulfilled up to that point:

Exodus 13:5 – "And it shall be, when Jehovah shall bring thee into the land of the Canaanites, and the Hittites, and the Amorites, and the Hivites, and the Jebusites, which he swore unto thy fathers to give thee, a land flowing with milk and honey."

Exodus 3:7-8 – "And Jehovah said, I have surely seen the affliction of my people that are in Egypt, and have

---

heard their cry by reason of their taskmasters; for I know their sorrows; and I am come down to deliver them out of the hand of the Egyptians, and to bring them up out of that land unto a good land and a large, unto a land flowing with milk and honey; unto the place of the Canaanites, and the Hittites, and the Amorites, and the Perizzites, and the Hivites, and the Jebusites."

Exodus 32:13 – "Remember Abraham, Isaac, and Israel, thy servants, to whom thou swarest by thine own self, and saidst unto them, I will multiply your seed as the stars of heaven, and all this land that I have spoken of will I give unto your seed, and they shall inherit it forever."

God swore to give the land to Abraham: "And Jehovah spoke unto Moses, Depart, go up hence, thou and the people that thou hast brought up out of the land of Egypt, unto the land which I swore unto Abraham, to Isaac, and to Jacob, saying, unto thy seed will I give it" (Exodus 33:1).

Moses confirmed the land covenant in Exodus 34:9-11, which says, "Pardon our iniquity and our sin, and take us for thine inheritance. And he said, Behold, I make a covenant: before all thy people I will do marvels, such as have not been wrought in all the earth, nor in any nation; and all the people among which thou art shall see the work of Jehovah: for it is a terrible thing that I will do with thee. Observe thou that which I command thee this day: behold, I drive out before thee the Amorite, and the Canaanite, and the Hittite, and the Perizzite, and the Hivite, and the Jebusite."

The land was given to those who "walked forty years in the wilderness, till all the nation, even the men of war that came forth out of Egypt, were consumed, because they hearkened not unto the voice of Jehovah: unto whom Jehovah swore that he would not let them see the land which Jehovah swore unto their fathers that he would give us, a land that flowed with milk and honey" (Joshua 5:6).

The promise from God to Abraham was complete with the receiving (inheriting) of the Promised Land.

Judges 6:9 – "I delivered you out of the hand of the Egyptians, and out of the hand of all that oppressed you, and drove them out from before you, and gave you their land."

Israel had the land as a possession; they just had to take it with the help of God.

Deuteronomy 1:8 – "Behold, I have set the land before you: Go in and possess the land which Jehovah swore unto your fathers, to Abraham, to Isaac, and to Jacob, to give unto them and to their seed after them."

The verse above references the first time Israel came to the Promised Land and turned back. Forty years later, they were given another chance. The only thing they had to do was take possession.

Joshua 1:11 – "Pass through the midst of the camp, and command the people, saying, Prepare your victuals; for within three days ye are to pass over this Jordan, to go in to possess the land, which Jehovah your God giveth you to possess it."

Israel first took possession of the land of Canaan as the Promised Land just before the first Passover in the Promised Land.

Joshua 21:43 – "So Jehovah gave unto Israel all the land which he swore to give unto their fathers; And they possessed it, and dwelt therein."

Three actions are presented: God gave, Israel possessed, and Israel settled. First, God promised Israel the land. Second, God brought Israel from Egypt to the Promised Land where they then possessed it. Lastly, Israel must remove all inhabitants so they can settle the land.

Judges 2:1 – "God said, I made you to go up out of Egypt, and have brought you unto the land which I swore unto your fathers."

When all Israel crossed the Jordan to possess the Promised Land, the promise made 400 years before was fulfilled.

God has given Israel all the land promised; however, they must possess it, which is Israel's responsibility.

Deuteronomy 7:1-2 – "When Jehovah thy God shall bring thee into the land whither thou goest to possess it, and shall cast out many nations before thee, the Hittites, and the Girgashites, and the Amorites, and the Canaanites, and the Perizzites, and the Hivites, and the Jebusites, seven nations greater and mightier than thou; and when Jehovah thy God shall deliver them up before thee, and thou shalt smite them; then thou shalt utterly destroy them: thou shalt make no covenant with them, nor show mercy unto them."

Deuteronomy 8:1 – "Go in and possess the land which Jehovah swore unto your fathers."

Deuteronomy 9:1-3 – "Hear, O Israel: thou art to pass over Jordan this day, to go in to dispossess nations greater and mightier than thyself, cities great and fortified up to heaven, a people great and tall, the sons of the Anakims, whom thou knowest, and of whom thou hast heard say, Who can stand before the sons of Anak! Know therefore this day, that Jehovah thy God is he which goeth over before thee as a devouring fire; he will destroy them, and he will bring them down before thee: so shalt thou drive them out, and make them to perish quickly, as Jehovah hath spoken unto thee."

The entire land promised would not be conquered until King David and his son King Solomon as seen in 2 Chronicles 9:26 and Kings 4:21. All the land of Canaan was given to Israel, but it was their responsibility to take it. Moses warned them that if they did not take it all, they would not live in peace.

The moment Joshua laid rocks of remembrance from crossing the dry Jordan and performed the religious Passover, they were awarded their first lot of land in the Promised Land. From this, they branched out in conquest of the whole land of Canaan. Joshua and the Israelite battle the inhabitants of Canaan until the land was divided, ushering in the first Jubilee. Scripture highlights the moment of the fulfillment of the 400 years:

Joshua 1:2 – "arise, go over this Jordan, thou, and all this people, unto the land which I do give to them, even to the children of Israel."

Joshua 1:11 – "Pass through the midst of the camp, and command the people, saying, Prepare you victuals; for within three days ye are to pass over this Jordan, to go in to possess the land, which Jehovah your God giveth you to possess it."

Judges 2:1 – God said, "I made you to go up out of Egypt, and have brought you unto the land which I swore unto your fathers."

The 400 Years and 430 Years Are Not the Same Events

The 400 years given in Genesis 15:13-16 and the 430 years given in Exodus 12:40-42 should not be clustered into the same event but rather separate events. To begin with, they do not represent the same amount of time. There is a 30-year discrepancy between the two. In addition, each duration represented an entirely different endpoint.

The Genesis time cluster of 400 years started when God made the covenant with Abraham and continued until Israel entered the Promised Land. The 430 years mentioned in Exodus marked the 430th anniversary from the day Abraham left his hometown of Ur to the Exodus from Egypt.

From this point forward, this book will consider the covenant between Abraham and God in Genesis 15:13-16 as one event that started with God's promise and was fulfilled with Israel's arrival in the Promised Land. In addition, this book will evaluate Exodus 12:40-42 as its own timeframe marking the duration between Abraham's departure from Ur to the Children of Israel's departure from Egypt.

Calculating Abraham's Events

Abraham's life has three significant events that can be calculated.

1. When he left the city of Ur.
2. When God made a covenant with Abraham.
3. Abraham's age when he left the city of Ur.

The first date to examine is when Abraham left Ur and moved into the Promised Land. One needs two things: the date to begin at and the length of time to that event. In order to find the answer to both of these, we will examine the following verse:

Exodus 12:40-42 – "Now the time that the children of Israel dwelt in Egypt was four hundred and thirty years. And it came to pass at the end of four hundred and thirty years, even the selfsame day it came to pass, that all the hosts of Jehovah went out from the land of Egypt. It is a night to be much observed unto Jehovah for bringing them out from the land of Egypt: this is that night of Jehovah to be much observed of all the children of Israel throughout their generations."

The 430-year sojourn of the Children of Israel included much of Abraham's life and started when he first came to Canaan and would continue through the Egyptian captivity. The Exodus event from Egypt is also the first Passover. This date is April 16, 1524 BC (see appendices A and B to see how this was calculated).

By taking the morning of Saturday, 15 Nissan, 1524 BC, and subtracting 430 years from it, gives us 15 Nissan, 1954 BC, which, in our calendar, is April 28, 1954 BC.

On April 28, 1954 BC, Abraham left the sinful city of Ur. Then exactly 430 years later on Saturday, April 17, 1524 BC, the Children of Israel left Egypt on the first Passover. Both of these dates are the same because, by the Jews calendar, it is 15 Nissan. Our calendar makes it look like different dates, but the Israelite calendar is the same day.

Moses showed the similarities of their exit from sinful Egypt to the Promised Land with Abraham's exit from the sinful city of Ur to pursue God's promise. The paralleled plight built a link between Israel and their patriarch father, Abraham.

The second date to find would be the date God made a covenant with Abraham.

Genesis 15:13-16 – "God said unto Abram, know of a surety that thy seed shall be sojourners in a land that is not theirs, and shall serve them; and they shall afflict them four hundred years; and also that nation, whom they shall serve, will I judge: and afterward shall they come out with great substance. But thou shalt go to thy fathers in peace; thou shalt be buried in a good old age. And in the fourth generation they shall come hither again: for the iniquity of the Amorites is not yet full."

From the moment Abraham entered the covenant, there would be 400 years until his descendants return. Using the Exodus date of Saturday, April 17, 1524 BC, and adding 40 years gives the date that they "come hither again" in April of 1484 BC, the 40th anniversary of exiting Egypt and the first day that Abraham's descendants celebrated their Passover in the Promised Land. The next step will be to subtract the prophetic 400 years from 1484 BC gives us 1884 BC.

Thus, 1884 BC would be when God and Abraham ratified the covenant that God had alluded to many years prior.

Based on findings within appendices A, B, and C, one can construct a timeline from Abraham to the Promised Land entrance.

1. Starting with the Exodus date of 1524 BC and adding 40 years to it gives us the year that Israel entered the Promised Land, being 1484 BC.

2. Subtracting 400 years from the entrance to the Promised Land in 1484 BC we get a date when the covenant between Abraham and God was established being 1884 BC.

3. Using the base date of the Exodus, we can subtract 80 years for Moses and two years for the Pharaoh, who did not know Joseph, giving us the date for Joseph's death as 1606 BC.

4. Subtracting 110 years for Joseph's life found in Genesis 50:22 gives us Joseph's birthday as 1716 BC.

5. Joseph's father, Jacob, at the time Joseph was born was 91 years old, so by subtracting 91 years, Jacob's birth year is 1807 BC.

6. Genesis 25:26 informs us that Isaac was 60 years old at Jacob's birth, so Isaac's birth year is 1867 BC.

7. Abraham's birth can be found in Genesis 21:5. Abraham was 100 years old when Isaac was born. This gives Abraham a birth date of 1967 BC.

An examination of the family tree shows its viability.

The land covenant between God and Abraham occurred when Abraham was roughly 83 years old. This makes sense, seeing as Abraham was 75 years old when his father died, and he was 85 when he conceived his first son with Hagar. This provides a window of ten years for when the event must take place. The events before the covenant shows that roughly eight years would be needed. Abraham would then need roughly two years for Ishmael to be conceived at 85 years of age. Using this rough figure, Abraham was roughly 83 years old in 1884 BC.

Abraham would have been born in 1967 BC and exited Ur in 1954 BC, giving him an age of about 13 years of age. This figure makes sense, seeing 13 is often considered an age of accountability. Abraham circumcised his son at the age of 13 in Genesis 17. The Bible informs us that when Jesus was 12 years old, he went to the temple as it was customary in those times and was accidentally left there. The Jews in modern times also have a bar mitzvah at the age of 13. When Jews reach the age of accountability, frequently 13 years old, and choose to follow God, they have a bar mitzvah.

The same idea is often followed in Christian churches. Often, when children are raised in a church, they choose to follow God and be baptized around 13 years of age. I was raised in the church, and by the time I reached 12 years of age, I chose to follow Jesus. I chose to follow Jesus even though I legally had to go where my parents went and live where my parents lived. Even though I was still dependent on them to meet my needs, I still chose with all of my ability to follow God, giving Him credit for all.

Abraham, being 13 years of age, would not want to live on his own. When Abraham's father left Canaan, he would have wanted to take Abraham with him. The act of Abraham choosing to go with his father when he left the sinful city of Ur pleased God.

Lining up all biblical dates and years, a timetable can be constructed that meets the Bible's criteria. This timeline can now be used to compare biblical events to other timelines.

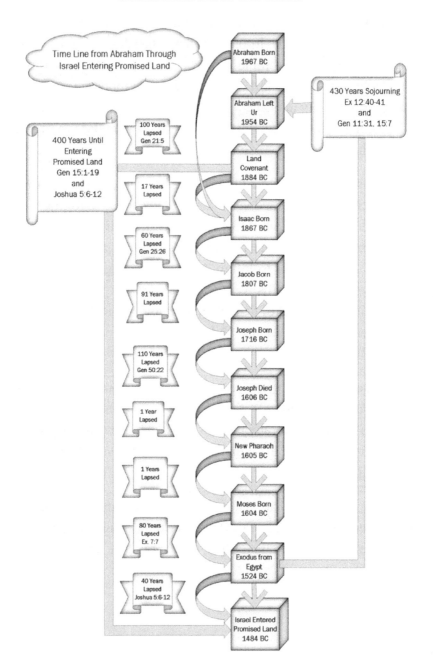

Time Line from Abraham Through
Israel Entering Promised Land

Abraham Born
1967 BC

430 Years Sojourning
Ex 12:40-41
and
Gen 11:31, 15:7

Abraham Left
Ur
1954 BC

100 Years
Lapsed
Gen 21:5

400 Years Until
Entering
Promised Land
Gen 15:1-19
and
Joshua 5:6-12

Land
Covenant
1884 BC

17 Years
Lapsed

Isaac Born
1867 BC

60 Years
Lapsed
Gen 25:26

Jacob Born
1807 BC

91 Years
Lapsed

Joseph Born
1716 BC

110 Years
Lapsed
Gen 50:22

Joseph Died
1606 BC

1 Year
Lapsed

New Pharaoh
1605 BC

1 Years
Lapsed

Moses Born
1604 BC

80 Years
Lapsed
Ex. 7:7

Exodus from
Egypt
1524 BC

40 Years
Lapsed
Joshua 5:6-12

Israel Entered
Promised Land
1484 BC

Author's Note

Dear Reader,

Thank you for reading *Solar Eclipses in the Bible*. I pray that this book is a blessing to you as it has been to my family and myself. My fervent desire is that this study has strengthened you spiritually. If this book's ministry has blessed you, I pray that you will share this book with others. You can help others find this book by writing a review at the location this book was purchased.

If you would like to learn more about solar eclipses in the Bible please visit: BibleEclipses.com.

If you have any questions please email me at:

Mail@JeffreyGrimm.com

Sincerely,

Jeffrey Grimm

Bibliography

Barnes, Albert. *Notes: On the Book of Job, Vol. I.* New York: Leavitt, 1849.

Barnes, Albert. *Notes: On the Whole Bible.*

Barton, George A. *Archeology and the Bible.* Philadelphia: American Sunday-School Union.

Burr, Jonathan Kelsey. *A Commentary on the Book of Job: Intended for Popular use.* New York: Phillips & Hunt, 1879.

Clarke, Adam. *The Holy Bible: A Commentary and Critical Notes, Vol. III, Job to Solomon's Song.* New York: Carlton and Phillips, 1853.

Clarke, Adam. *The New Testament: A Commentary and Critical Notes.* New York: Myers, 1835.

Clarke, Adam. *The Holy Bible: A Commentary and Critical Notes, Vol. II, Joshua to Esther.* New York: Lane & Sandford, 1842.

Easton, M. G. *Illustrated Bible Dictionary.* New York: Harper and Brothers, 1893.

Edersheim, Alfred. *The Life and Times of Jesus the Messiah, Vol. I.* New York: E. R. Herrick, 1920.

Ellicott Charles John ed., Stanley Leathes. *An Old Testament Commentary for English Readers, vol. IV, Job.* New York: Cassell and Company, 1884.

Ellicott, Charles John ed., Plumptre. *Commentary for English Readers, Vol. V.* New York: Cassell and Company, 1884.

Ellicott, John ed., Payne Smith, *A Bible Commentary for English Readers, Vol. I, Book of Genesis*. New York: Cassell, 1882.

Exell, Joseph S. *The Pulpit Commentary, I Kings*. New York: Funk and Wagnalls.

Gill, John. *An Exposition of the New Testament*, 1746-1748.

Grimm, Jeffrey. *Solar Eclipses in the Bible*. United States: Jeffrey Grimm 2021.

Hastings, James. *Dictionary of the Bible*. New York: Charles Scribner's Sons, 1909.

Josephus, Flavius. Translated by Whiston, *The Works of Flavius Josephus: Antiquities of the Jews*. London: John Bumpus, 1828.

Lias, j. j. *The Cambridge Bible for Schools and Colleges*. Cambridge: University Press, 1884.

Mackenzie, Donald. *Egyptian Myth and Legend*. London: Gresham Publishing Company, 1907.

Maclaren, Alexander. *Expositions of Holy Scripture: The Book of Judges*. London: Hodder and Stoughton.

Maunder, E. Walter. *The Astronomy of the Bible: An Elementary Commentary on the Astronomical References of Holy Scripture*. London: T. Sealey Clark, 1908.

NASA, Fred Espenak and Jean Meeus. *Five Millennium Catalog of Solar Eclipses: -1999 to +3000 (2000 BC to 3000 CE)* – Revised (NASA/TP-2009-214174). NASA, JANUARY 2009.

NOAA. *"NOAA Scientists Get Rare Chance to Study the Effects of an Eclipse on Weather."* n.d. Welcome to NOAA Research.

Accessed April 20,2021. https://research.noaa.gov/article/ArtMID/587/ArticleID/57/NO AA-scientists-get-rare-chance-to-study-the-effects-of-an-eclipse-on-weather.

NOAA, US Department of Commerce, NOAA. n.d. *"Solar Eclipse Day Storm Summary – August 21 2017."* www.weather.gov. Accessed April 20, 2021. https://www.weather.gove/fsd/20170821-severestorms-solareclipse.

Ottley, Richard R. *A Handbook to the Septuagint.* London: Methuen, 1920.

Poole, Matthew. *Annotations upon the Holy Bible, Vol. I.* London, 1700.

Perowne, J. S. The Cambridge Bible for Schools and Colleges. Cambridge: University Press, 1896.

Parker, Joseph. *The People's Bible: Discourses Upon Holy Scripture, Vol. XI, The Book of Job.* New York: Funk and Wagnalls, 1889.

Plunket, Emmeline M. *Ancient Calendars and Constellations.* London: John Murray, 1903.

Vinke, Peter. continuation of Matthew Poole's Commentary. *Annotations upon the Holy Bible.*

Rodkinson, Michael L. Translated. *New Edition of Babylonian Talmud, vol 3.* Boston: New Talmud Publishing Society, 1916.

Rodkinson, Michael L. Translated. *New Edition of The Babylonian Talmud, vol VII, "Festivals".* Boston: New Talmud Publishing Company, 1899.

Seiss, Joseph A. *Gospel in the Stars: Or, Primeval Astronomy.* New York: Charles C. Cook, 1910.

Strong, James. *Dictionaries of the Hebrew and Greek Words.* New York: Eaton & Mains, 1890.

Ussher, James. *The Annals of the World.* London: Tyler, 1658.

Wesley, John. *Explanatory Notes*, 1754-1765.

Wilson, Robert. *"What Does the Sun Stood Still Mean?"*. Moody Monthly, October 1920.

About the Author

I have been a student of the Bible and a follower of Jesus Christ for over 30 years. My wife, son, and I continually strive to become stronger in faith as we follow Jesus Christ together. I am a seeker of the truth; in other words, I want to know what the Bible says.

I worked in the aerospace industry for 20 years. I enlisted in the United States Air Force, where I was an avionics maintainer on the B2-A Stealth Bomber aircraft. Upon exiting the United States Air Force, I went to work as a contractor for the Ground-Based Midcourse Defense (GMD) as a missile computer operator.

The more I studied the Scripture and learned the laws of physics, which is a way to mathematically calculate the world that God made and governs, the more I realized how much God loves us!

Made in the USA
Las Vegas, NV
26 February 2024

86292356R10138